P9-EDL-227

Algrove Publishing Limited
36 Mill Street, P.O. Box 1238
Almonte, Ontario
Canada K0A 1A0

Telephone: (613) 256-0350
Fax: (613) 256-0360
Email: sales@algrove.com

Cover photo of the Wye Mill is by Allen Davis.
Copyright 2004 Allen Davis - Allen Davis Photography.
This mill is located in Wye Mills, Maryland. The overshot wheel powers a grist mill on a site first used for a mill in 1671.

National Library of Canada Cataloguing in Publication

Overshot water wheels for small streams / edited by Leonard G. Lee.

(Classic reprint series)
"Bulletin no. 70."
Includes index.
Reprint of Fitz steel overshoot water wheels. Originally published: Hanover, Pa. : Fitz Water Wheel Co., 1928; and of an excerpt from the 7th ed., rev., of A treatise on hydraulics. Originally published: New York : Wiley, 1902.
ISBN 1-894572-94-7

1. Water-wheels--United States. I. Lee, Leonard G. II. Series: Classic reprint series (Almonte, Ont.)

TJ862.O84 2004 621.2'1 C2003-906772-6

Printed in Canada
#1-1-04

Overshot Water Wheels for Small Streams

Edited by Leonard G. Lee

Table of Contents

Appendix

Publisher's Note

The era of water wheels is long past but the fascination remains. Part of the charm of water wheels is the fact that they are non-polluting in use. Water is merely interrupted in its passage to a lower level with virtually no temperature change and no pollution introduced.

Efficient overshot wheels were introduced near the end of the era of water-powered mills. John Fitz, the founder of the *Fitz Water Wheel Company*, did much to popularize this style of wheel by improving the design to maximize efficiency. The great value of the 1920's Fitz catalog reproduced here is the extensive coverage of installations all over the U.S., particularly the smaller farm installations. Throughout the text, real and potential water wheel problems are discussed and recommended solutions are given. It is an excellent primer for anyone considering a water wheel for a small stream.

Many people reading this book will not be familiar with water wheels in general or where the overshot style fits into the wide range of wheel types. Overshot wheels are particularly suited to low flow streams. They adapt well to varying discharge rates and their efficiency exceeds all other wheel or dynamo types *"...in the development of small powers"*, to quote the Fitz catalog.

Since the total text of the catalog ran to only 84 pages, we included related material from a hydraulics text of the day dealing with wheel efficiency and, finally, a chapter on turbines just because it covers turbine design at Niagara Falls, a hot topic a century ago.

Leonard G. Lee
Publisher and Editor
January 2004
Almonte, Ontario

Major Water Wheel Types

Overshot Water Wheel

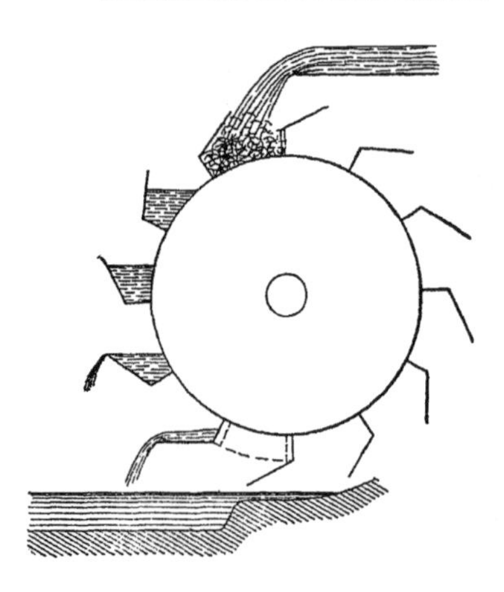

The most efficient of all wheel types, it maintains its efficiency (at times even increasing it slightly) as water flow diminishes. Of all the types, it is the style most applicable to small streams. Efficiency can exceed 90%.

Breast Wheel

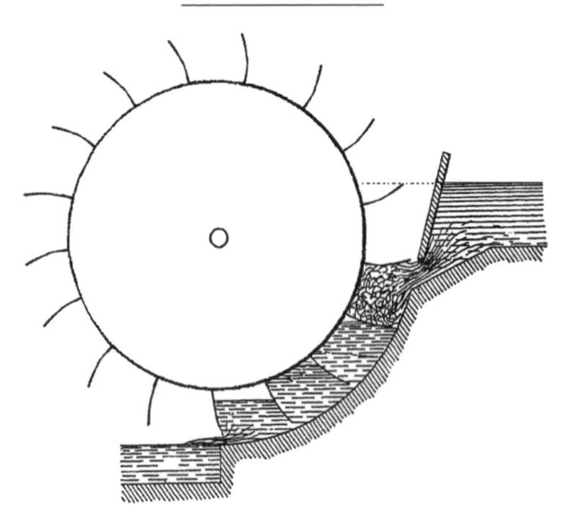

Suited to small falls, it functions partly by impulse and partly by weight of the water. Efficiency ranges from 50% to 80%.

Undershot Wheel

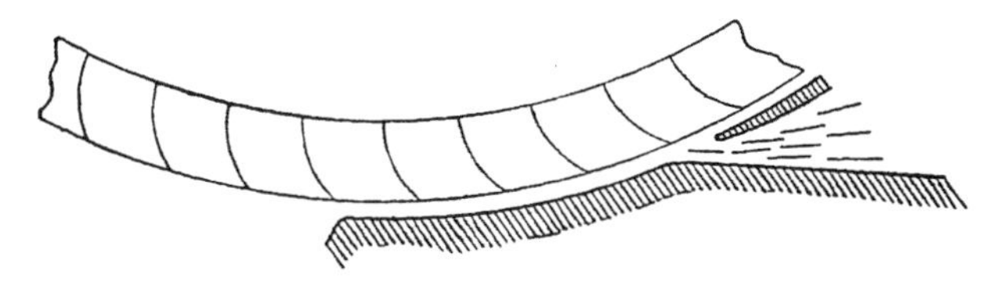

Sometimes used on an anchored scow in a stream where efficiency is less than 50%, it can reach as much as 60% if it is confined flow and has curved vanes as illustrated.

Vertical Impulse Wheel

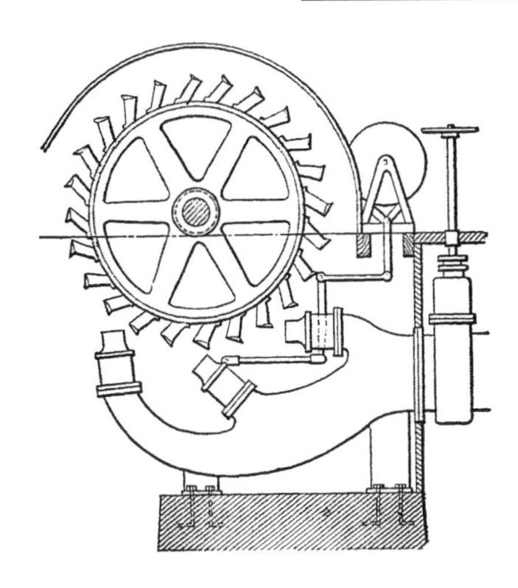

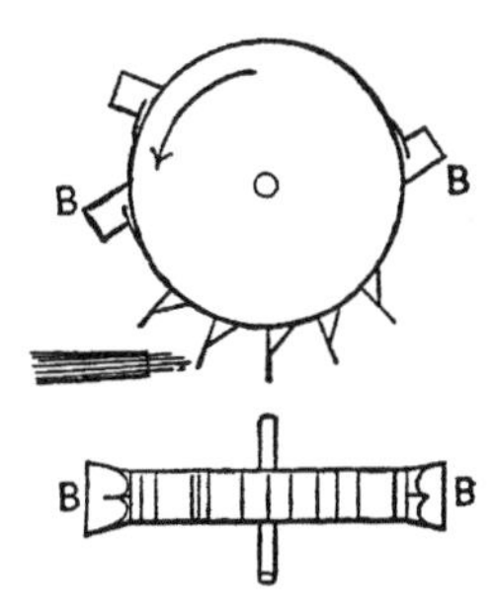

Similar to an undershot wheel but used with high heads, the water introduced to the wheel from a jet or jets in good designs can reach 80% efficiency.

Horizontal Impulse Wheel

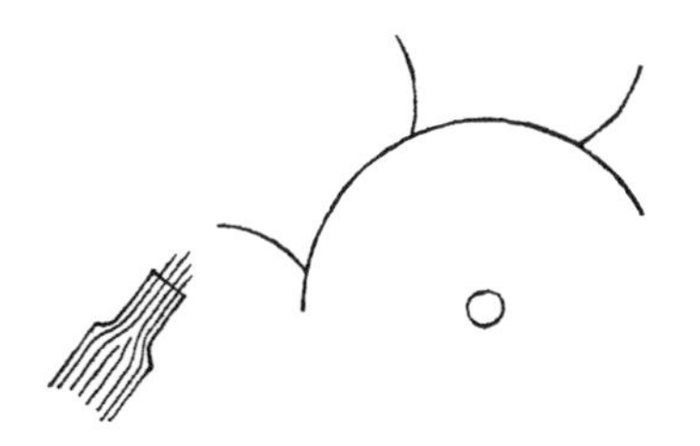

Horizontal wheels operate under the same general principles as downward flow wheels, all described in greater detail in the Appendix.

BULLETIN NO. 70

Fitz

Steel Overshoot

Water Wheels

MANUFACTURED BY

FITZ WATER WHEEL CO.

HANOVER, PA., U. S. A.

JOHN FITZ, *Inventor and Manufacturer.*

Born, April 15, 1847—Died, April 12, 1914

" He originated the modern Steel Overshoot Water Wheel, and rescued from oblivion one of the most useful principles of Hydraulics."

A Bit of History

The Fitz I-X-L Steel Overshoot Water Wheel is the product of three generations of unbroken experience in the design and manufacture of water wheels. Its high efficiency is due to its correct mechanical principles and to its careful design and construction.

The manufacture of Overshoot Water Wheels was begun by Samuel Fitz, in Hanover, Penna., U. S. A., in the year 1840. The industry has been carried on continuously since that time on the same site under the management of the son and grandson of the original founder.

The earlier Fitz Wheels were, of course, built of wood. A number of orders are still being received for iron parts for wooden water wheels, as described later in this booklet, but by far the greater part of the business done today is the manufacture of the all-steel Overshoot Water Wheels, in which the company specializes.

The real credit for the invention of the modern Steel Overshoot Water Wheel and for its development into its present highly efficient form must be given to the late John Fitz. Very early in his business career he realized the great possibilities of this type of water wheel and he devoted the greater part of his life to the study of its principles and the improvement of its efficiency. How well he succeeded is shown by the high regard in which the Steel Overshoot is held today. In spite of this, we have not relaxed our efforts for further improvements, but are constantly striving for still better results in every detail of construction.

The knowledge and experience accumulated by our organization during its long career in the water wheel business forms an even greater asset than our well equipped modern factory. Most of our employees have grown up with us, and our millwrights and mechanics have been trained in this line from early youth. In reckoning with your water power problems, therefore, we have a vast fund of practical experience to draw from and we are glad to place this freely at the service of our customers.

Sincerely yours,

FITZ WATER WHEEL COMPANY,

J. S. Fitz, President,
C. F. Ehrehart, Treasurer,
Chas. E. Ehrehart, Secretary.

"Wheatsworth Mills" at Hamburg, N. J., the home of Wheatsworth Whole Wheat Flour and other well-known F. H. Bennett Products. This very modern plant uses two 20 ft. diameter by 12 ft. wide Fitz Steel Overshoot Water Wheels to drive the milling and elevating equipment. A third Fitz Wheel equipped with Fitz Automatic Governor, operates the electrical equipment.

General Information About Overshoot Water Wheels

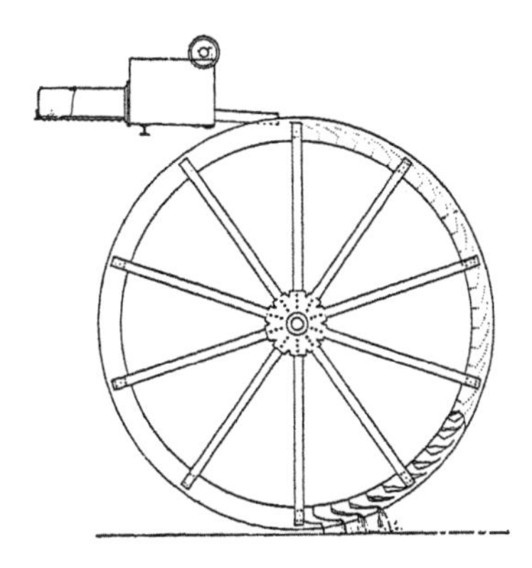

The Overshoot Wheel derives its power directly from the force of gravity. The illustration shows the principle upon which it works. The weight of the water which is admitted to the buckets, loads one side of the wheel, causing it to revolve.

The water should be applied to the top of the wheel at a point about ten inches back of the vertical center line, so that the buckets will fill up just as they pass over the topmost point of the wheel.

The diameter of an overshoot wheel should be from 2½ to 3 ft. less than the total fall available. By total fall, we mean the vertical distance from the surface of the water in the forebay or "tank" above the top of the wheel, down to the surface of the water in tail race or discharge canal, below the bottom of the water wheel.

Wheels of all these types were formerly built of wood. Many picturesque examples of this method of construction are still to be found in rural districts. The overshoot wheel possessed so many advantages that it soon displaced the other early types of water wheels. Even with all its crude design and ill-suited material, the wood overshoot still persists as a strong competitor of the modern small turbine.

The field of the Overshoot Wheel lies in the development of small powers. It is not suitable for use in very large developments on account of the increase in size and weight of the wheel as the head and discharge are increased beyond certain limits. It can be built in any diameter needed up to 60 ft. and in any width desired up to a capacity of 3,000 cubic feet per minute in single units.

The power of an overshoot wheel depends upon both the diameter of the wheel and the width of the wheel. The larger the diameter of an overshoot wheel, the more power it will develop with the same amount of water. The wider the wheel is made, the more water it will accommodate. The relative power of two wheels of the same diameter is of course in direct proportion to the amount of water each wheel is capable of using, if other conditions are equal. The question of determining the proper size wheel to use for any particular location is one which should usually be left to the judgment of the builder of the wheel. We do not publish any list of sizes of wheels in this booklet for the reason that we prefer to have our customer give us the data asked for on page 62, so that we, ourselves, can select the size of wheel he ought to have.

For any location within the range of its capacity, the overshoot type of wheel possesses certain decided advantages over all other types of water wheels, viz.:

(1) High efficiency.
(2) Adaptability to varying discharge.
(3) Simplicity.
(4) Reliability.

The extent to which any overshoot wheel makes use of these advantages depends largely upon the design of the wheel, its accuracy of construction and the material of which it is made. The Fitz Steel Overshoot Water Wheel makes use of the same basic principles as the old wood overshot, but its superior design enables the Fitz Wheel to develop more than 90% efficiency as compared with the 60% to 70% efficiency of the wood wheel. The reasons for this are set forth in detail later on in this booklet under the heading "Comparison with wood wheels." The efficiency of the Fitz Wheel is not a matter of opinion or guess work. Our wheels are rated according to the results shown by rigid tests in Hydraulic Testing Flumes.

Developing an efficiency of 90% or more, the Fitz Steel Overshoot is vastly more efficient than any other type of water wheel known. In the smaller installations especially, where the overshoot most frequently competes with a turbine, it is doubtful whether the turbines ever operate with an efficiency higher than 70%. It is true that many turbine builders claim high efficiencies for their wheels, but every experienced turbine user has good reason to know how far the turbines themselves fall short of their makers' claims when confronted with actual running conditions. In every case, where the amount of fall and quantity of flow is suitable for our type of wheel, a Fitz Overshoot will develop at least one-third more power than any turbine working under similar conditions, or 25% more than the best new wood wheel that can be built.

The above statements are made without prejudice to the turbine type of water wheel, for we build a turbine wheel ourselves that ranks fully equal to the best on the market. We are just as glad to sell a turbine wheel as we are to sell an overshoot where the conditions are suitable for a wheel of that type, but we will not furnish either kind for a location where we know that our customers' interests require the other.

30 ft. dia. by 3½ ft. face Fitz Steel Overshoot Water Wheel driving mill of Capt. D. W. Barger, at Shawsville, Va. This wheel is fed by a wooden forebay and is equipped with a segment gear.

Fitz Water Wheels have brought prosperity to water power mills throughout the country for they afford steady power and constant service from streams that would be worthless with any other type of wheel.

There are more than 750 mills and factories in the State of Virginia alone that are being driven today by Fitz Water Wheels.

Fitz Overshoot Water Wheel partially installed at South End of Beebe Lake Dam, Cornell University, Ithaca, N. Y. A hole 3 ft. wide x 2 ft. high, cut thru the abutment, supplies the concrete flume.

Old in Principle, Thoroly Modern in Practice

The development of the overshoot water wheel into its present state of unrivalled efficiency has been the result of many years of thought and effort. Founded in its present location nearly ninety years ago, this firm has been building water wheels continuously during all that time, but it has never ceased to improve and modernize its product.

Up until the advent of the modern Fitz Steel Overshoot Water Wheel an efficiency of 60% to 70% was considered remarkably good for a small water power plant. Today, practically every recent text-book on hydraulics concedes an efficiency of 90% or more to the "modern steel overshoot water wheel when properly constructed." Proper construction means "Fitz Construction," for no other make of water wheel has approached this high efficiency. Fitz Water Wheels form part of the equipment of some of the greatest engineering colleges and universities of the world. They have been adopted by many railroads and by many of the leading engineering firms in this country for use wherever high efficiency and perfect reliability are the essential requirements in a small water power development.

Fitz Steel Overshoot Water Wheel in actual operation at Philadelphia Sesqui-Centennial using Morse Silent Chain Drive in connection with General Electric D. C. Generator. Grand Medal of Honor awarded this exhibit.

Field Demonstration Plant used by New York State College of Agriculture. All of the electrical equipment shown is operated by means of the electric current supplied by the Fitz Water Wheel.

Results of Laboratory Tests at University of Wisconsin

A ten-foot diameter Fitz Steel Overshoot installed in the Hydraulic Laboratory of the University of Wisconsin has received an unusually thoro series of tests, as described in detail in one of the University's Bulletins.

A range of four hundred per cent in variation of the amount of water supplied to this water wheel, showed a difference of only 5% in the efficiency of the wheel. We quote as follows from an article in the "Engineering News" of January 2, 1913, by Prof. Carl R. Weidner, Instructor in Hydraulic Engineering at the University of Wisconsin:

"To engineers familiar with the variation in efficiency of the turbine at part gate, a glance at the curves obtained from the Wisconsin experiments will be convincing as to the superiority of the overshoot wheel in respect to its adaptability to varying discharge."

"The result of the experiments * * * * * * * * show high efficiencies under a wide range of operating conditions. Reliable tests of turbines have been reported yielding as high as 89% efficiency but it is rarely that this figure is obtained in an actual installation. In the smaller plants, especially, where an overshoot wheel would be capable of competing with a turbine, it is doubtful whether the turbines operate with an average efficiency higher than 70%."

Fitz Water Wheel in the Testing Flume at the University of Wisconsin.

"Laboratory tests of a machine, when properly interpreted, undoubtedly have a great value, but it must be borne in mind, that any test so made represents results under the exact conditions of the test. The conditions under which the Wisconsin experiments were performed approached practical conditions very closely. The wheel tested was of a standard pattern taken from the stock of the manufacturers. The structural features are simple, and none of these features, of the wheel itself, were changed during the tests. * * * * * * * The results should, therefore, be readily duplicated in actual service, if the wheel is set properly."

The published test reports of the University of Wisconsin show that the ten ft. diameter Fitz Wheel above illustrated, mounted on our bronze-lined bearings, yielded an efficiency of 89%, on the water wheel shaft.

Later tests of this same wheel, made under the same supervision but with the mounting changed to our self-aligning ball bearings, showed an efficiency of 92%.

A Fitz Water Wheel, 20 ft. diameter by 5 ft. wide, driving an up-to-date ice plant for Mr. August Metz, Jr., of Milford, Pa.

An ice plant must have constant and reliable power. The Fitz Steel Overshoot supplies ample power at all times, without any cost, and requires very little attention.

Value of Water Power

A good water power is a valuable possession and the steadily increasing cost of fuel and labor are tending to make it more valuable every day. It costs at least seventy dollars per annum to produce one horse-power by steam by the most efficient methods. The average cost is much higher; about one hundred dollars usually for a small plant. A gasoline engine is even more expensive for continuous service.

With electric power for commercial purposes, selling at 4 cents per kilowatt or 3 cents per horsepower, a single horsepower used for only ten hours' service each day, will cost $90.00 per year, not even including the usual service charges, nor repairs or depreciation in the motor. Electric current for lighting purposes is usually sold thru a separate meter at from 10 cents to 15 cents per kilowatt, adding still more to the yearly bill.

This being the case, a water power developing ten horsepower is worth nine hundred to one thousand dollars a year; or the interest on an investment of nine to ten thousand dollars.

A sixty horsepower plant in a good location would have an earning capacity of six times the above, for that is what a similar sized steam plant would cost to operate, counting fuel, labor, repairs, interest and depreciation, etc. Figure it out for yourself on the basis of your own expenditures.

The power developed at any water power installation depends on three factors, viz.: The volume of water in the stream, the amount of fall and the kind of water wheel used. The first two factors are usually determined by the natural conditions and are nearly always developed to the greatest practicable extent. They fix the potential or theoretical power. The water wheel is the medium by which this potential or possible power is converted into actual profit-earning power.

There is a great difference in water wheels. Failure to realize this fact has caused many water power projects to result in disappointment. After spending, perhaps, thousands of dollars on the dam, race-way, flume, excavating, etc., to develop a power, it is a very poor policy to sacrifice a large part of the returns by putting in a wasteful, inefficient water wheel. A water wheel of low efficiency may only develop half, or less than half, the possible power of the location. That means a sacrifice of one-half the earning capacity of the plant. And that is just what nine-tenths of the turbines and wood wheels in existence are doing for their owners. The remaining tenth are doing better than this but not one of them is giving anything like the actual power it should give.

A man with a valuable water power cannot afford to take an inefficient wheel as a gift. His water power is valuable just in proportion to its earning capacity, and its earning capacity is regulated by the amount of power developed. A wasteful water wheel cuts down the value of the whole plant in proportion to the amount.

BUTLER QUARRIES, NEAR COCKEYSVILLE, MD.

A 16 ft. diameter x 5 ft. wide Fitz Steel Overshoot Water Wheel utilizes the water power of a famous old grist mill site to operate a large stone quarry, furnishing fine building stone for Baltimore.

FITZ WATER WHEEL AT THE GINGELL QUARRIES, NEAR EMMITTSBURG, MD.

The original grist mill was destroyed by fire, but the steel overshoot water wheel remained to do a more profitable business than ever before, by supplying power to a busy nearby rock quarry and crushing plant.

Selecting the Right Type of Water Wheel

A water power plant usually represents not only the investment of a considerable sum of money in the dam, race-way, flume, tail race, etc., but also in the value of the factory which it operates, since that can earn but little without the power. The cost of the best water wheel on earth is but a fraction of the value of the entire plant which depends on it. Too much care cannot be used in the selection of a water wheel. Only the best and most efficient on the market should be considered. That is the only wise and economical policy.

By repeated tests the Fitz Overshoot Water Wheel has shown that it will develop at least 33⅓ more power than the best turbine made using the same amount of water. We are well aware that some turbine builders claim from 80% to 85% efficiency for their wheels and pretend that this is proven by their records in the testing flume. Such claims are absurd. It is true that a few turbines have given a little over 80% efficiency in the laboratory when tested at full gate, but it must be remembered that these were large wheels built regardless of expense and working under the most favorable conditions known. Even in the case of the large turbines, the practical value of these tests may be seen from the fact that no two wheels of the same size and same make would give the same efficiency, and often the same wheel, when tested at different times, would vary considerably. Small turbines, such as our wheel competes with, have never shown good results even in a laboratory test.

It is well known that conditions are much less favorable to turbines in actual use than to those in the testing flume, and also that when you buy a turbine from any builder you don't get near as good a wheel as the one he builds especially to be tested. We know it to be a fact that there is no turbine built today that will develop over 65% to 70% efficiency in actual use, and the great majority fall much below this. See the extracts on following pages from some leading reference works in regard to this.

But it is not enough to merely consider the efficiency of a wheel with a full head of water. It is just as important to know how a wheel will act with a diminished head or scanty supply of water. No stream of water is of the same size at all seasons and a wheel that is not adaptable to varying conditions is useless a large part of the year. This is the point where all turbines, despite the claims of their makers, fail absolutely, for unless they are run at full gate, or nearly so, they will do very little work. The steel overshoot is a model wheel in this regard, as in every other respect, for it will run just as economically at one-fourth gate as at full gate, while when water is plentiful, it can be crowded far beyond its normal capacity.

The Fitz Wheel depends only to a small extent upon pressure for its power. It can adapt itself to a wide range of heads. This feature is especially valuable where water is scarce and a large pond is used to store the water over night. Every one knows how unsatisfactory it is to use a turbine where you have to run by heads. Since the turbine depends upon the pressure of the water, when the head diminishes naturally the speed diminishes and also the power. With the Fitz the head can be drawn down almost to the bottom of the race without affecting either the power or the speed.

Besides these most important considerations of high efficiency and adaptability to varying conditions, there are five other points that an ideal wheel should possess, viz.:

(1) Freedom from clogging and freezing.
(2) Tight gate.
(3) Perfect balance.
(4) Durability.
(5) Ability to do good work in back water.

These points are only to be found in the Fitz Steel Overshoot Water Wheel. The large buckets cannot possibly become clogged with leaves, sticks, or anything else, like turbine buckets, for whatever goes through the gate will pass over the wheel freely. Ice, which causes so much trouble with wood wheels and turbines, has but little effect upon the steel overshoot. It cannot form on the wheel as long as it is in motion, for the thin steel readily acquires the temperature of the water passing over it and remains above the freezing point. Even should any ice form on the wheel while standing, a few strokes with a hammer will cause the wheel to ring like a bell and will shiver the ice all off, for there is nothing for it to cling to.

The gate of our wheel is simplicity itself. It is tight beyond comparison with turbine gates. The balance of the wheel is very accurate. The wheel can be easily turned by one hand no matter how large it is. As for durability, it leaves nothing to be desired. The first wheels we ever built are still running and are in first-class condition right now.

Back water, which will soon stop a wood overshoot, has very much less effect on the Fitz wheel. We usually calculate our wheels to accommodate from one-fourth to one-half more water than the normal volume of the streams which drive them. Consequently at flood periods more water can be used on the wheel, thus overcoming the loss of head in back-water.

A careful consideration of the above facts must lead to the conclusion that the Fitz Steel Overshoot is not only the best water wheel on the market but also the cheapest, for it gives much the best value for the money expended. This wheel utilizes every bit of water to its fullest possible extent. The value of the increased power alone, that it yields, may be worth more every year than the whole cost of the water wheel, to say nothing of its greater durability and more satisfactory service.

This is an instantaneous photograph of a 16 ft. diameter by 7½ ft. face Fitz Steel Overshoot Water Wheel running at full speed and driving the mill at full capacity. Note the absence of splashing water. This is one of the peculiar merits of the Fitz. No water is wasted and there is no chance for ice to form on the walls or gear. Our internal segment gear is shown here driving jack-shaft in same direction the water wheel shaft runs.

HOW FITZ WATER WHEELS ARE SECTIONALIZED

See Detailed Explanation Under Heading of "Construction" on Pages 21 and 23

The Fitz Steel Overshoot Water Wheel

The Fitz Steel Overshoot Water Wheel is built entirely of iron and steel. Its high efficiency is due to its correct principles of design and to the high class workmanship and material used in its construction.

The word "Overshoot" is simply an arbitrary spelling which we adopted some time ago to distinguish our wheel from the ordinary "overshot" water wheel. For the sake of brevity our wheel is sometimes referred to by its old name, "The I-X-L," or often as "The Fitz Wheel."

We do not wish to convey the impression that the Fitz Overshoot is the best wheel for all locations or for all conditions. Our field is in the development and improvement of small water powers. By small water powers we mean those having falls of less than sixty feet and volumes of water smaller than 3,000 cu. ft. per minute for single units of wheels. Even within those limits, there are certain conditions to be met with occasionally which call for other types of wheels. Within its own field, however, there is no other type of water wheel in the world that can compete with the Fitz Wheel. Put your conditions up to our engineers and let us tell you what we can do for you. We will guarantee in every case to greatly improve your power or to let it alone.

The size of an overshoot wheel depends largely upon the situation, but we usually make the diameter about 2½ feet less than the amount of the actual working head.

The force of the water above our wheel is not lost but acts by its impulse upon the wheel just as it acts on a turbine or impulse wheel. In other types of overshot wheels this force is almost entirely wasted but the shape of our buckets and our method of applying the water to the wheel enable us to utilize this impulse. As will be seen from the cut on page eighteen, the water spurts across our smooth steel chute at a tangent to the crown of the wheel. It enters the bucket a little back of the vertical center line of the wheel and glides along the curved part of the bucket, striking the heel of the bucket at right angles to the radius of the wheel drawn to that point. Thus its power is communicated to the wheel in the direction best adapted to produce the greatest effect.

The curve of the bucket is not the same in all sizes of wheels. It is varied to suit the particular requirements. Proper allowance is made in all cases to permit the exit of air from the bucket when water is entering. The shape of the bucket is such as to retain the water until all possible power is taken from it. The water is actually retained in the buckets almost to the level of the surface of the tail race.

The housings of the steel overshoot, instead of coming flush with the buckets as in a wood wheel, are extended so as to prevent any water splashing over the sides. Thus not a drop of water is wasted and the water is discharged in the tail race with all its power extracted. Compare the calm stream flowing from the overshoot wheel with the rushing torrent discharged by the turbine and you will see one of our strongest points. Mighty few small turbines get more than 60% or 65% of the energy out

An old grist mill, built more than a century ago, converted into a modern summer home on the beautiful country estate of Messrs. S. D. and Robert D. Black, of the well-known firm of Black and Decker, Towson, Md.

A good water power site never ceases to be a valuable asset. This water wheel furnishes an ample supply of electricity for lighting, cooking, refrigeration, etc., for all of the buildings on the estate. The gearing is absolutely noiseless in operation and the plant is automatically controlled by a Fitz Governor.

of the water that they use, and the momentum of the tail race represents a considerable part of the remaining 35% or 40%.

Practically no power is wasted by friction in the bearings of our wheels. Fitz Wheels are so perfectly balanced and run with so little friction that a little child can turn the largest wheel we ever built, with one hand. Thus we are able to transmit undiminished to the jackshaft, nearly all of the energy we have extracted from the water.

With each wheel we usually furnish our "water-tight" iron gate and steel "chute." Our iron gate is a very valuable feature. On small streams in very dry weather, it is essential to save all the water possible. A wood wheel or a turbine will often allow enough water to leak away at night through its defective gates, to run a Fitz Overshoot for several hours a day. The Fitz gate consists of two parts, a smoothly planed iron frame, and a movable slab which is both planed and scraped to insure a very accurate fit. It is tight and at the same time it is almost perfectly trouble-proof. See illustrations on pages 69 and 70. The chute is the steel trough which carries the water from the gate to the buckets of the wheel. This piece is necessary in every case, in order to apply the water to the wheel at the proper tangent.

The object of all wheels is to utilize the weight of falling water and to develop power thereby. The Fitz Wheel does this in the most direct manner and therefore with the least loss. Turbines and other wheels, aim to develop their power in an indirect manner by reaction or impulse caused by pressure. To give even moderately good results they must be geared to run at certain speed, under a certain pressure and using a certain amount of water. On a variable stream, such as most are, these conditions are constantly changing, thus causing a great loss of efficiency to the turbine. Since the overshoot depends mainly on the positive weight of the water and only in a small degree on impulse, it can run fast or slow, with high head or low head, at full gate or fractional gate, with equally high efficiency, and developing power in exact proportion to the amount of water used.

The motion of the Fitz Overshoot is slow. In order to drive fast running machinery the wheel should be equipped with suitable gearing. Later on in this booklet, the reader will find a number of plans showing approved methods of connecting up various kinds of machinery to our wheels.

Construction

Fitz (I-X-L) Steel Overshoot Water Wheels are shipped "knocked down" in sections easy to handle. The rim or "buckets" comes in from eight to twenty sections, according to the diameter of the wheel. Every piece is carefully marked or numbered and we furnish full printed instructions for assembling with each wheel, as well as a blue-print drawing

10 ft. diameter by 3 ft. wide Fitz Steel Overshoot driving Electric Light and Power Plant for Mr. Frank B. Moore, Trenton, N. J.

showing the setting. The arms are numbered to suit the pockets of the flanges to which they belong. The sections of the rim and the segments of the gear are likewise numbered to correspond with their respective positions. The illustration on page 18 will show our method of marking.

We can furnish a skilled mechanic from our factory to install our wheels when wanted, but our careful method of marking and the perfect "fit" of each piece makes it very easy for the purchaser to install the work himself.

The center flanges or hubs are made of cast semi-steel with dove-tailed sockets to receive the arms, and are keyed on the shaft with two keys each. To these flanges are bolted the arms, which are of best Open Hearth steel.

THE EQUALITY MILLS OF MARTINSBURG, WEST VIRGINIA

A Fitz Steel Overshoot, built by John Fitz in 1870 for this mill, is still in use. At the old Fitz Foundry, across the creek from this mill, the first iron wheel ever built (by Samuel Fitz, in 1852), is still in service.

The iron regulating gate and steel chute supplied with our wheels are illustrated and described on pages 69 and 70. The bolts and rivets used in our wheels are selected with great care. They are absolutely the best that can be bought. For specially heavy service we make our bolts out of nickel-chrome-vanadium steel. Patented Nut Locks are used wherever necessary. Our gears are cast from semi-steel in our own foundry and are much stronger and tougher than cast gearing.

Comparison With Turbines

With a large stream of clear water which never varies in volume, and with a good fall, a well made turbine will work very satisfactorily. It is true that the efficiency of small turbine water wheels is always overrated—very few of them in practical use giving over 60% of the power they should develop—but of course where there is an abundance of water it is not necessary to be economical. But on a light stream, or wherever it is

MILL OF P. O. VOGLER, AT FALL CREEK, WISCONSIN

Here a 20 ft. diameter by 10 ft. face Fitz displaced a 24 inch turbine used less than three months. With 401 cu. ft. of water per minute, the Fitz does exactly the same work that the turbine did when using 797 cu. ft. per minute. At full capacity the Fitz uses less water than the turbine at full capacity and yet drives additional machinery which formerly required the assistance of a 30 H. P. Otto Gasoline Engine to help out the turbine.

In accordance with our usual practice in very cold climates. the water wheel was located inside of the mill building. The point marked X on the side of the mill represents the approximate position of the water wheel shaft.

desirable to get the full power from the water, they are failures. The capacity of a turbine is unchangeable. If you have more water than you need, it is wasted. If less, it will hardly turn the wheel. The reverse is true of the Fitz, as its adaptability to varying conditions is one of its strongest points. When water is scarce it will develop the full percentage of power, while with an abundance of water the wheel can be crowded far beyond its normal capacity.

A turbine depends for its power upon the reaction or impulse of the water discharged under pressure of the working head. The pressure is due to the weight of the water and is proportional to the working head of water over the wheel. The higher the head the greater the pressure, and hence the velocity of the water discharged. The wheel must run at a certain proportionate velocity, the buckets must be curved at a certain angle, and the water must be discharged in a certain volume in order to do good work. All these points must be right in order to obtain even 60% to 70% efficiency. They are fixed by the volume of the stream to be used and the amount of water to be secured. Most streams are constantly varying in volume and it is impossible to supply the wheel with the same amount of water or to keep up the same head, so the conditions are seldom favorable for a turbine to reach its maximum efficiency. It cannot adapt itself to the changed conditions of diminished supply or lowered head. Consequently in dry weather, when economy of water is most necessary, the turbine is most wasteful, and will do practically no work at all.

Of course we are aware that all turbine manufacturers table their wheels at 80% efficiency, or higher, and that nearly every one claims that he alone has solved the impossible problem of making a turbine to work equally well at partial gate as at full gate. These foolish claims are a result of conditions established many years ago. Since it is the universal custom, the turbine man who did not make such claims could get no hearing for his wheel. The customer has usually no means of testing his wheel and does not realize the outrageous discrepancy between the power promised by the turbine men, and the results actually attained.

An interesting side light on some of the losses which make impossible the high efficiency of any turbine wheel is shown by the following extract from a book entitled "Turbine Water Wheel Tests," written by Robert E. Horton, and published (1906) by the United States Geological Survey. ("Water Supply and Irrigation Paper No. 180") page 22:

"This waste (of the gross power of the water by the *better class* of turbines) is due to the following causes:

(1) Shaft Friction.
(2) Skin Friction on the Guides and Bucket Surfaces.
(3) Leakage through Clearance Spaces, etc.
(4) Terminal Velocity of the water on leaving the wheel.
(5) Production of Swirls or Vortices in the water within the turbine, some of the energy being thus converted into motion which is ineffectual in producing power. How this occurs is illustrated in Fig. 12, (after Vigreux)."

Remember that these losses occur in every turbine. Some of them are quite important. Take for instance the one item of leakage through only one of the clearance spaces. Even a perfectly new turbine wheel has some clearance between the runner and the case. Water escaping through this opening under very heavy pressure and carrying sand and grit, soon enlarges this clearance until it is ¼″ wide or more. Take a 20″ turbine under 24 ft. head. That means a stream of water ¼″ thick by 63″ (the circumference of the wheel) under a pressure of 24 ft. escaping all the time without ever going through the buckets at all. The gate leakage is also a heavy item of loss.

The terminal velocity of the water discharged from any turbine is always great and denotes a considerable waste of power. Of course it is impossible to shape the buckets so perfectly as to divert all the energy from the water delivered to them, consequently a large part of the power always escapes to the tail race.

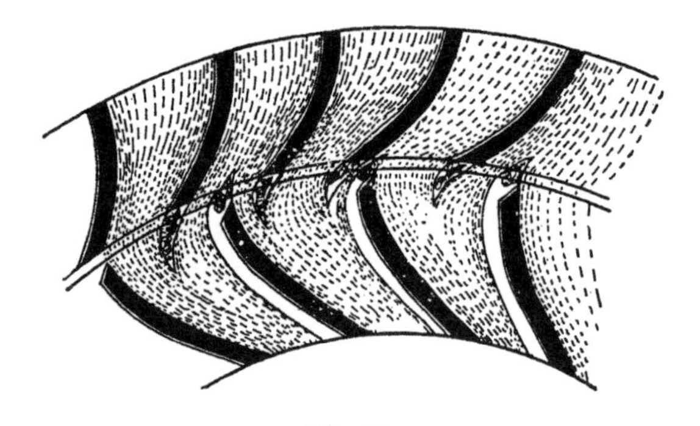

Fig. 12
Diagram Showing Interference and Formation of Eddies in a Turbine
Borrowed from " Turbine Water Wheel Tests." Printed by U. S. Geologic Survey

Referring again to the cut, the reader will note the swirling motion of the water within the turbine, which occurs even under the most favorable conditions, such as when running at full gate. When the gates are partially closed, the direction of the water is slightly changed and the water no longer strikes the buckets at the proper angle. At such times the swirling motion is much intensified and a large part of the energy of the water is consumed in working against itself. This is one of the main causes of the great loss of efficiency which occurs in a turbine when it runs at part gate.

Unwin, in his great work " On the Development of Water Power," (page 140) gives the following table of losses which occur in a turbine. It is to be remembered that a turbine which has been in use a few months will hardly do nearly this well, and when running at part gate there can be no comparison.

Character of Loss	Percentage
Shaft Friction and Leakage	10 to 15
Unutilized Energy	6 to 7
Friction and shock in Guide and Wheel Passages (i. e., skin friction and internal motion)	10 to 15
Total	26 to 37

The Fitz Steel Overshoot Water Wheel will deliver at least a third more power than the best turbine using the same amount of water, because it develops its power by utilizing the weight of the water in the simplest and most direct manner possible, instead of indirectly through impulse or reaction, as in the turbine. The water is received from the forebay in such a manner as to utilize as much as possible of the impulse due to the head in the forebay, and is retained by the correctly curved water-tight buckets until it reaches the center again at the bottom, where it is discharged in a calm stream with all the energy extracted. There is no occasion for loss of power in this process; no splashing, no leaking or spilling too soon.

40 ft. diameter by 2 ft. face Fitz Steel Overshoot Water Wheel in mill of Thompson & Carter, Shepherdstown, W. Va., driving 35-barrel mill with 90 cu. ft. of water per minute. There is no storage dam here. The water comes direct from a large spring. A turbine wheel would be absolutely worthless here.

If half the normal quantity of water is used on a Fitz Overshoot wheel it will develop half the power, or one-fourth the power with one-fourth the water, thus showing that its efficiency is unimpaired by the changed conditions. No power is lost by friction, for a child can turn our largest wheel with one hand.

On an ordinary stream, in the course of a year's run, the Fitz Overshoot will do nearly twice as much work as a small turbine. It will give a third more power than the turbine at full gate, and at partial gate it will give two to three times the power, depending upon the quantity of water used.

A great deal of trouble is experienced by turbine users in hilly or sandy localities where the frequent floods and freshets wash down great quantities of sand and grit, which are very hard on their wheels. The leaves, sticks and other trash which get into the buckets and choke up the narrow vents are also a constant annoyance and frequently stop the wheels. The turbine flume, if built of wood, requires constant attention and repairs. The gates are invariably leaky after a few months' use and waste a great deal of water. The complicated construction of some turbines make them particularly apt to get out of order, but they all give more or less annoyance in this regard.

None of these troubles have any effect whatever upon the Fitz Steel Overshoot. There is nothing about it to break or get out of order. Every part is exposed to view and easily accessible, but the only attention required is to oil the bearings occasionally. The gate is as near perfection as possible for anything which has to work in water, and owing to its simple construction will remain for years just as tight as the day it was put in. The large buckets cannot possibly choke up no matter how dirty the stream is, for anything that will pass through the gate will pass over the wheel without the slightest injury.

The condensed experience of thousands of water power owners shows that if you have more water at all seasons of the year than you can use, so that economy of water is no object to you, then you can use a turbine satisfactorily, provided you are not greatly troubled with sand or trash in your stream. But if you want to get all out of your water power that

Sheppards Mills, near Bridgeton, N. J., owned by Mr. Geo. F. Geisinger. A 14 ft. diameter by 6 ft. wide Fitz Steel Overshoot Wheel has taken the place of two modern turbines and enables the owner to dispense entirely with the Fairbanks-Morse Oil Engine which formerly ran most of the time.

there is in it; to develop the highest efficiency at all times, no matter how low the water is; if you want durability and freedom from repairs; economy and satisfactory results, then the Fitz Steel Overshoot Water Wheel is the only wheel on the market worthy of your consideration.

A 13 ft. diameter by 16 ft. wide Fitz Wheel driving a paper mill in connection with a 400 H. P. steam engine.

As an auxiliary power the Steel Overshoot has no rival. This wheel is helping out a 400 H. P. engine. It runs constantly, twenty-four hours a day, using the natural flow of the stream and assisting the engine at all times to the full extent of the water power. No matter how low the creek gets, it is always capable of saving a good deal of coal when used in this way. The wheel adapts its speed perfectly to that of the engine. It cannot hold back as a turbine would do when water gets scarce. A Fitz Wheel will synchronize just as well with a gasoline engine or motor as it will with a steam engine. A turbine is worse than useless in a place like this, for most of the time the engine would have to be pulling the wheel along in addition to driving the plant.

Automatic Speed Regulation

To drive an electric light plant, a turbine should be equipped with an automatic governor. No water wheel can be governed successfully unless its capacity is considerably larger than that of the maximum load it has to drive. Otherwise there will be no reserve power for the governor to call upon when the head goes down or when back-water occurs, etc.

A turbine that is large enough to be governed properly, must therefore be running at part gate nearly all of the time, and consequently its ordinary wastefulness is still further increased. On the contrary, a Fitz Overshoot will maintain its high efficiency when run at any fraction of its capacity. (See efficiency curve chart on page 43.) Fitz Governors afford perfect automatic regulation, and save every bit of the surplus water.

18 ft. diameter by 8 ft. wide Fitz Overshoot.

Ancient mill sites throughout the land are being restored to usefulness and prosperity by means of Fitz Water Wheels.

In localities where there is no market for grist mill products, old water power sites like this are being converted into hydro-electric plants to light nearby villages and farms. Wood wheels are absolutely worthless for such purposes because they can not be kept in balance and it is impossible to govern a wood wheel.

Comparison With Wood Wheels

The wood overshoot still survives as an active competitor of the small turbine in some parts of the country. On a light stream, a well made wood wheel will often give better results than a turbine, but it always falls far short of getting the full possible power from the water.

Wood is not a fit material to use in building a water wheel. A high efficiency wheel must be made of metal. Wood overshoots have been built for centuries, but up until the advent of the Fitz, an efficiency of 75% was considered the limit for an overshoot wheel of any kind. Mighty few wood wheels ever approach that efficiency today.

The buckets of a wood wheel cannot be shaped to a suitable curve to receive and discharge the water properly. A wood wheel is invariably out of balance and its jerky motion is destructive to good results from the machinery it operates. The constant swelling and drying of the wood soon causes all parts to get loose: the buckets leak: and a considerable proportion of the energy is wasted.

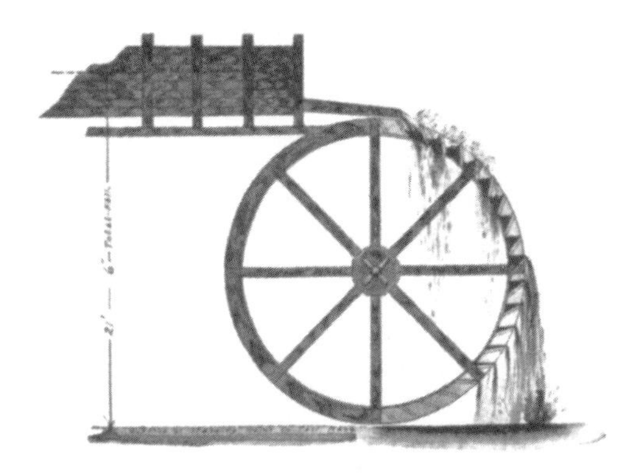

WASTEFUL WOOD WHEEL

Snap-shot Photo of 12½ ft. diameter by 9 ft. face Fitz Steel Overshoot Water Wheel, running at full speed and driving mill of Bruce Bros., at Gormeley, Ontario, Canada. Please note the absence of splashing water. This is one of the " differences " that marks the superiority of the Fitz over the old-fashioned overshoot wheel.

In installing this wheel, the concrete penstock which held the former turbine was used as shown. The water is brought to the penstock thru a round steel flume laid right on the ground. In the concrete penstock the water rises up to the same level as the water in the dam and is carried out to the Overshoot by means of a short wood forebay built out to receive our iron gate and chute. This extension in other cases is frequently made of iron or even of concrete.

In a steel wheel, the buckets can readily be shaped to suit the design required. The Fitz steel bucket is shaped so as to receive the water at the crown of the wheel with the least possible shock. It retains the water to a point just a little above the level of the tail race. In other words, the water gets to work on a Fitz wheel at least three buckets earlier than it does on other wheels, and it stays on the wheel from three to ten buckets longer, depending upon the diameter of the wheel.

A wood wheel gets no benefit from the head of water over the top of the wheel. In order to put the water into the thick, straight, wood buckets, the chute is generally slanted a good deal and the water is allowed to "drop" on to the wheel in the manner illustrated on page 31.

ECONOMICAL FITZ WHEEL

The water consequently strikes the wheel at an ineffective angle and its energy is dissipated in shock, instead of being communicated to the wheel.

This loss is more serious than the casual observer would suppose. In the case of a 14 ft. diameter water wheel, for instance, the total head is usually at least 16 or 16½ ft. Two feet of that total head are in the depth of the water in the forebay over the top of the wheel. If the water wheel does not utilize that 2 ft. of head (and a wood wheel never can), then it is wasting 12 or 12½% of the power at this point alone.

The illustration of the steel wheel on this page, or better yet, the larger cut on page 18 will show clearly how the water is applied to a Fitz Wheel. Our steel chute is set nearly level. The water glides over the smooth steel with very little loss by friction, and shoots into the steel buckets in a direction just tangent to the crown of the wheel. Its energy is thus applied to the wheel at the most effective angle. The buckets are given just the right curve to enable them to receive the water with the least possible waste of power by "shock." Study the photos on pages 17, 31 and 36 showing Fitz Wheels, photographed while running, and compare these wheels with the splashing, sloppy, leaky wood wheels to be found everywhere.

In cold weather, ice gathers on the arms and shaft of a wood wheel,

Snap-shot Photo of Fitz Water Wheel running in exposed location in Northern New York. This is not a fair test, since the wheel should be installed inside of building in such climates and the water should be brought to the wheel in a water-tight flume or steel tank. However, in spite of the old-style leaky wood forebay, and the utter lack of protection from weather, please note the failure of any ice to cling to the water wheel itself.

putting it to a terrible strain and often causing it to stop running. Every one who has attempted to cut ice from a wood wheel knows what a difficult and dangerous job it is and how frequently it must be done in a severe winter. Wood is a non-conductor of heat and altho the water which is running over the wheel is usually warmer than the freezing point, the wood wheel will gather ice rapidly along its housings and arms. The water splashing over the sides of the wheel freezes on the shaft and walls. The ice freezes right into the pores of the water-soaked wood, and is very difficult to dislodge.

Ice does not affect the steel wheel, because steel is a good conductor of heat. The steel buckets readily assume the same temperature as the running water and they communicate that temperature to the housings and soling, so that no ice will gather on the wheel while running. Even if, thru a leaky forebay, some ice is allowed to form on the wheel standing idle at night, that ice will wash off the wheel when the water is turned

Fitz Water Wheel in operation at Marlboro Mills, Marlboro, N. Y., on State Highway Route 9-W. Note water-tight Fitz Steel Flume and Forebay Box, in connection with freedom from ice.

on in the morning. Ice cannot get into the pores of the steel, and hence has no opportunity to cling to it like it does to wood.

In very cold countries, we house the wheel in, so as to protect it from the cold winds. The friction of the running water liberates a certain amount of heat in the wheel room and prevents any trouble from anchor ice. The freedom of the Fitz Wheel from ice of all kinds is one of its strongest points. Neither the turbine nor the impulse wheel can compare with it, in its immunity from trouble with slush ice or frazil ice.

Our wheels are in most successful use all along our extreme northern border and in many provinces of Canada, in situations where a wood wheel would be impossible, and where turbines have proven very troublesome on account of ice.

About six inches of the fall is usually wasted in the slant of a wood chute and the clearance between the floor of the chute and the inside of the buckets. This space is all saved in a steel wheel. Several inches can be frequently gained at the bottom of the wheel for the reason that the steel buckets require less clearance from the tail race. We build all our wheels to suit the locations where they are to go and are glad to advise our customers as to the proper size wheel to fill their individual requirements.

A wood wheel is completely paralyzed by a little back-water. Our smooth steel buckets create much less friction than wood buckets when wading in back-water. They are ventilated so as to avoid creating a vacuum when discharging the water, and consequently do not suck up water as a wood wheel does. We rate our wheels at the power they develop with buckets filled only ¾ full. When it is necessary for them to run in back-water, the buckets can be filled up full. One of our 17 ft. diameter wheels driving the pumping plant of the Hanover & McSherrystown Water Co., near our town, frequently wades in back-water to a depth of six feet without affecting its work. Water is plentiful at such times and more can be used on the wheel to overcome the loss of head.

A water-soaked wood wheel weighs three times as much as a steel wheel and the friction of the bearings is many times greater. Standing idle for one day, the wood wheel absorbs water on one side and is then out of balance. Its jerky motion wastes both water and power. No machinery requiring a smooth, even speed can be driven successfully with it. It is impossible for a Fitz Wheel to get out of balance. It runs so smoothly that its speed can readily be controlled by the Fitz Automatic Water Wheel Governor.

The life of a wood wheel is short, not much over ten years as a rule. The old-time wood wheels lasted longer, but the old-time material is no longer available, and the old-time millwright is fast disappearing. A Fitz Wheel will outlast a number of wood wheels. The metal wheels we built in 1852, at our old shops at Martinsburg, W. Va., are still in active service today.

The one excuse that a wood wheel has for existence today, is its supposed cheapness in first cost. Even that claim is frequently without foundation. The manifold advantages of steel wheels in every other respect will far outweigh any difference in cost, to the man who is looking for actual value.

10½ ft. diameter by 11 ft. wide Fitz Water Wheel, direct-geared to Goulds Triplex Pump, furnishing the entire city water supply system for Marlinton, West Virginia. This plant runs constantly, day and night, and requires no expense or supervision except for occasional oiling or repacking of the pump. This photo was taken with water wheel running at full speed.

17 ft. diameter by 4½ ft. wide Fitz Steel Overshoot Water Wheel driving the plant of the Hanover and McSherrystown Water Company at Hanover, Pa. This company is a subsidiary corporation of the North American Water Works Corporation of New York City, which uses Fitz Water Wheels to drive five of its plants in various towns. More than 1,000 Fitz Water Wheels are at work in Pennsylvania alone.

Pumping Plants

The high efficiency and great adaptability of the Fitz Steel Overshoot make it the perfect motive power for a pumping plant. For high elevations we use a triplex pump with the crank shaft connected direct to the water wheel shaft. This gives the water wheel a tremendous leverage. No matter how low the supply stream gets, the water wheel will continue right on at work.

A Fitz Overshoot Pumping Plant has a wide range of speed and capacity, that makes it ideal for municipal water works requirements. In case of a fire or any other emergency the plant can be run at nearly double its ordinary capacity by simply speeding up the water wheel, while at other times if desired, the speed can be reduced to the same extent.

This cannot be done with any other type of water wheel. Nor can the over-all efficiency of a Fitz Pumping Plant be approached by any other type of pumping plant in existence. Under exactly similar circumstances a Fitz Plant will usually deliver 50% more water than can be pumped by a turbine or ram, and in the majority of cases we have greatly excelled this figure.

Municipal Pumping Plant for Borough of Kennett Square, Pa., driven by a Fitz Water Wheel.

Nothing can get out of order in regard to a Fitz Wheel. Nothing can get loose. Leaves or trash or sticks or slush cannot choke it. It keeps right on at work thru floods and droughts when any other kind of wheel would be out of service entirely. We know of plants equipped with our wheels that have run for years, day and night, without any attention except occasional oiling and re-packing the pumps.

Driving a good-sized pumping plant is a pretty severe test for any water wheel. The power required varies sharply from time to time.

Where a long pipe is used, air may accumulate where there are dips in the line, and what is known as "water-hammer" results. At such times the pressure may double or treble almost instantaneously, throwing a tremendous strain on the wheel. This is often sufficient to stop a turbine

Second Fitz Pumping Unit installed recently for the Mohnsville Water Co. to supply the towns of Mohnton and Shillington, Pa.

The first Fitz Overshoot, installed twenty years ago, is still in continuous operation, although the volume of business has grown over 500% since the first unit was installed. The two Fitz Wheels, with the assistance of the new dam, are still handling the entire load without the aid of any auxiliary power, and with only one man to look after the entire plant and handle all the office work and collections in two large towns.

or to tear the gears to pieces. The damage to motors and switches and automatic devices in an electric-driven plant can easily be imagined.

The overshoot has a great advantage here by reason of its adaptability in speed and great momentum and leverage, which makes it impossible to stall the wheel. The great strength and superior construction of the Fitz enable it to withstand any strain like this with ease, while a poorly constructed water wheel, under the same conditions, would be racked apart.

Fitz Water Wheel Pumping Plants afford an ideal service for isolated plants where the highest efficiency and the greatest reliability are desired. They require far less attention than any other plant on the market, and many of our largest plants receive no supervision at all, other than a 15-minute weekly inspection and oiling.

Municipal Water Works Plant at Frenchtown, N. J., driven by Fitz Water Wheel installed in 1911. The old buildings were completely destroyed by fire in 1927, but the service was not interrupted, as the Fitz Water Wheel kept right on at work. The new building was erected over the same old equipment.

The absolutely unrivalled efficiency of the Fitz Pumping Plant enables one of these units to pay for itself many times over in any location where a large volume of water must be pumped. As compared with a ram or with a turbine, we have never failed to pump from 50% to 100% more water, operating under just the same conditions. Besides this advantage, the Fitz Wheel can be used with any kind of auxiliary power, whether steam, gas, or electric, without the least difficulty.

The eminently satisfactory work of the Fitz Wheel is shown by the fact that we have furnished wheels for seven municipal pumping plants for a single corporation operating a number of water works plants in this State. The Pennsylvania Railroad, Lake Shore & Michigan Southern Railway, the Norfolk & Western Railway, the Chesapeake & Ohio Railway, the Virginian Railroad, and numerous large hotels, schools and colleges, are also among our customers, besides hundreds of small towns and villages and large estate owners.

We have installed a number of very small plants for private persons to pump water for country residences, etc. We build wheels for this purpose as small as two feet diameter. The same features which make the Fitz Wheel so desirable for large plants apply with equal force to these miniature installations.

While Fitz Plants are sold purely on their economic merits, they lend themselves extremely well to picturesque landscape schemes. On some of the finest country estates in America, the Fitz Water Wheel that drives the pumping system, has been made one of the most attractive features of the grounds.

Pumping Water on a Large Country Estate.

THE FITZ DIRECT GEARED TO A GOULDS TRIPLEX PUMP

The combination of a Fitz Steel Overshoot Water Wheel with a good Triplex Pump in the above manner is the nearest thing on earth to a pure gravity plant. An outfit like this needs practically no attention beyond occasional oiling and repacking of the pump glands. It will pump fully 50% more water on an average than any turbine, ram or other water power device ever built.

We can arrange our wheels to connect up to any type of pump now in place when desired, but we prefer in most cases to furnish the complete pumping unit as above shown.

20 ft. diameter Fitz Water Wheel driving pump to furnish water for Mr. P. S. DuPont's Longwood Gardens, near Kennett Square, Pa., thru four miles of pipe line.

16 ft. diameter by 1¼ ft. wide Fitz Water Wheel installed by the Tennessee Mill & Mine Supply Company to operate water supply system for the suburban village of Westmoreland Heights near Knoxville, Tenn. This plant delivers an abundant and unfailing supply of water thru two miles of pipe against a head of 180 ft.

Water Supply Systems for Country Homes

Pumping plants for small farm houses or for great country estates or for summer hotels, should deliver the same reliable and efficient service that engineers insist upon in municipal water works plants. Any interruption or break-down in the service is bound to be both expensive and annoying. A Fitz Pumping Plant is peculiarly free from troubles of all kinds and will continue right on at work under conditions that would soon stop any other plant.

As compared with a hydraulic ram, the original cost of a Fitz Water Wheel Plant is, of course, considerably higher, but the difference in service is beyond comparison. The Fitz Plant will pump much more water than a ram, and to far greater elevations. It cannot clog up with leaves or sticks. With a Fitz Plant, it is absolutely impossible for the spring water in the pump to become contaminated by contact with the brook water that drives the water wheel. That frequently happens in the case of a ram, thus causing grave danger of serious epidemics.

Another very important advantage in a Fitz Pumping Plant for country homes is the fact that we can pump into a pressure tank in the basement of the residence, using air pressure to force water at any desired pressure to any part of the buildings. This system enables the architect or engineer in many cases to dispense with any need for an expensive reservoir or unsightly tower to create the necessary pressure.

As compared with an electric motor driven pump, the advantages of a Fitz Plant are very obvious. There is no expense to be considered for power, no interruption from lightning or sleet storms, and no fuses or motors to replace.

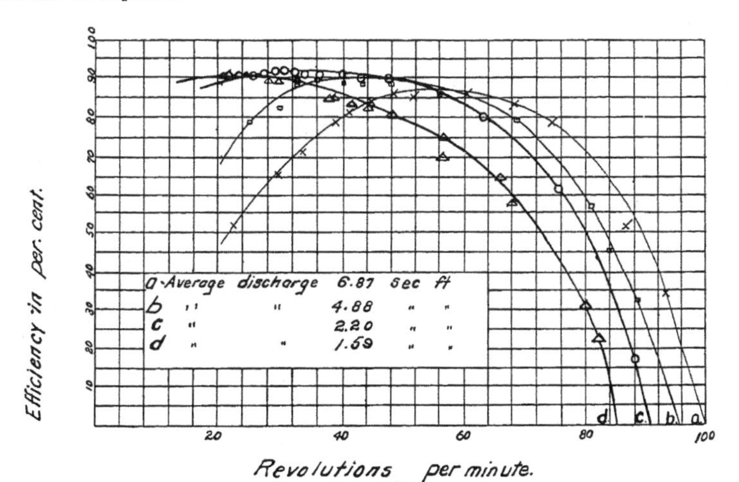

EFFICIENCY DISCHARGE CURVES

6 ft. diameter by 1 ft. wide Fitz Water Wheel, mounted on Timken Roller Bearings, and using Morse Silent Chain to drive Myers Self-Oiling Bulldozer Pump for farm and dairy supply. This photo was taken on the farm of Mr. J. B. Miller, at Parkton, Md. We have furnished 15 plants of this same size to the Chicago, Milwaukee & St. Paul Railway Co., to pump water for their water towers in Nebraska and South Dakota.

Fitz Overshoot Pumping Plant on beautiful country estate of Mr. Irving Brokaw, at Mill Neck, near Oyster Bay, L. I. The pump house was designed to harmonize with the architecture of the mansion nearby.

Combination pumping plant and electric light plant on fine country estate near Wilmington, Delaware. This not only pumps water for the great dairy barns and greenhouses and gardens, but also furnishes an ample volume for the big water tank of the Pennsylvania Railroad to supply their locomotives.

Combination pumping and electric light plant on "Hilandale Farm" of Mr. John H. Danby, Chadds Ford, Pa.

Fitz Steel Overshoot in course of installation for Wheatsworth, Inc., of New York City.

40 ft. diameter by 8 ft. wide Fitz Water Wheel driving the Hydro-Electric Plant for Dahlonega, Ga.

Hydro-Electric Plants

In an electric lighting plant the power required varies probably more than in any other line of business known. For a few hours in the evening when the maximum load is on, probably five or six times as much power is needed as at other times. An electric generator consumes power in approximate proportion to the amount of current that is being taken from it. A Fitz Water Wheel uses water just in proportion to the amount of power it is developing. Hence the two are adapted to each other perfectly. When a comparatively small amount of current is being used, a comparatively small amount of water is required to operate the wheel, and the surplus can be accumulating in the dam or storage pond for use during the period when the maximum amount is required. Thus it is possible for a plant to operate continuously, selling current all day long for power and lighting purposes. This adds greatly to the profits of the business, for the increased revenue is all gained without any extra running expense or additional investment.

No other wheel on the market can do this. It is the wonderful adaptability of the Fitz Wheel and its response to varying demands that make it the ideal wheel for this purpose. It will develop a third more power than the best turbine using the same amount of water, even at full capacity. That is when a turbine is at its best. At half gate, the efficiency of a tur-

A pair of twin Fitz wheels each 12½ ft. diameter by 11 ft. face, driving Hydro-Electric plant at Callaway, Neb. This pair of wheels furnishes power to drive 150 bbl. flour mill of the Callaway Mill and Electric Co. by electricity, and also power to light the town of Callaway about one mile distant. The plant is kept in operation twenty-four hours a day, and seven days in the week.

bine is cut in half, as every one knows, but that of the steel overshoot remains undiminished in the least. In electrical work it is necessary to run at part gate most of the time, for the maximum load is attained only for a few hours, and even then there must always be some power in reserve. At its best the efficiency of a turbine is low. In an electric lighting plant, it seldom has an opportunity to attain its best. In a situation where a turbine will use up all the water in a few hours, the steel wheel will run all day. Where economy of water is a feature to be considered, no one can afford to use anything but the modern steel overshoot.

The great momentum of the Fitz Wheel and its perfect balance, cause it to yield a smooth, steady motion, well suited to electrical machinery. Small variations in the load do not affect it as they do a turbine.

The use of a Fitz Steel Overshoot Water Wheel will enable the owner of an electric light plant on a small stream to get at least double the service from his water power that he can obtain in any other way. This is the only type of water wheel that can be made big enough to carry the maximum flow of the stream without wasting a tremendous amount of

Cooks Falls Electric Co., Inc., lighting Cooks Falls, N. Y., and Roscoe, N. Y., with 27 ft. Fitz Water Wheel.

water when running under a light load. Countless tests under the supervision of skilled engineers, as well as years of practical experience, have shown how wasteful a turbine water wheel must be at less than half gate capacity. The Fitz Steel Overshoot, under similar tests, has shown that it will maintain the same high efficiency at any stage of part gate, down to one-tenth of its capacity or even less.

This means that the Fitz Steel Overshoot can be run all day long, maintaining twenty-four hours' service in many locations where a turbine could be run only a few hours a day. In daylight hours, while the overshoot is running at part capacity, the surplus flow of the stream can be accumulating in the pond for use when needed.

The new Fitz Automatic Water Wheel Governor, only recently perfected, will regulate the flow of water to the wheel in exact accordance with the demands of the generator. By means of this governor the voltage and speed are maintained on a constant basis without requiring change or supervision.

Home-made log dam on Deer Creek, Md., to supply water to a 9 ft. diameter Fitz Overshoot Water Wheel, supplying power for electric lighting, cooking, and refrigerating for three homes.

Even a little stream like this can light a farm house. A 6 ft. diameter Fitz Overshoot in this little building supplies the farm house and large poultry houses of Mr. Paul G. Sellers, Unionville, Pa.

Loss in Transmission of Power from Fitz Wheels

It will be noted from the photo on page 11 that provision was made in the University of Wisconsin Tests to measure the power of the water wheel not only on the water wheel shaft but on the " jack-shaft " or countershaft. The loss in transmission of the power by our system of spur gearing was shown to be from 2½% to 3%.

Contrast this slight loss in the high efficiency of the Fitz Overshoot with the much heavier loss in the transmission of power from a turbine wheel, by bevel gears. That loss is variously estimated at from 15% to 25% even by turbine builders. To avoid this loss, the horizontal turbine was brought out some years ago, but horizontal turbines are notoriously so inefficient that most turbine manufacturers now recommend the use of the vertical wheel in spite of the bevel gearing its use entails.

It will be remembered, of course, that we are speaking of small turbines. Theoretically, the small turbine should be just as efficient as its bigger brother of similar type, but actually it is not nearly so efficient. The tests on which turbine builders base their claims of efficiency are based on the work done by large turbines under exceptionally favorable conditions. The builders assume in their catalogs that their smaller wheels are just as efficient as their large wheels and their power tables are based on this assumption. The result is, that every turbine builder in America greatly overrates the powers of his smaller wheels, no matter how nearly accurate may be the rating of his 36" wheels and larger sizes. There is no room for argument on this point. Any one who has ever had any practical experience with a small turbine knows that this is a fact, especially if he has had an opportunity to measure its work on the switchboard of an electric plant or to compare it with the work of a steam engine or Fitz Wheel of the same rated capacity.

Of the two types of turbines, the vertical wheel is of course much more efficient than the horizontal one. If we assume that the small vertical turbine may develop as much as 70% efficiency (and that is a very liberal allowance) we must deduct from this figure, at least 15% of the net power to cover the loss in transmitting the power through bevel gears to the horizontal shaft. That leaves only 59½% of the possible power of the stream delivered to the horizontal shaft.

As against this figure, contrast the 89% net power, which the Fitz Overshoot delivers to the horizontal jackshaft through its spur gear.

Methods of Connecting Up Fitz Wheels to Various Kinds of Machinery

The illustration on the fifth page of this booklet shows a Fitz Wheel without gearing of any kind. Most machinery requires a high speed, and to attain this it is necessary to use a gear of some kind on the water wheel. The quickest method of getting up speed, especially in the case of a high diameter wheel, is to use a segment gear bolted to the arms of the water wheel as shown on page 54. On that page we show a water wheel completely installed with a segment gear and belt drive to a line shaft from which all other machinery can be belted.

The segment gear shown in this illustration is an "External Gear" with the cogs on the outside of the circle as shown. A gear like this will drive the jackshaft and pulleys in the opposite direction to that in which the water wheel is traveling.

The water wheel shown on page 17 is equipped with an "Internal Segment Gear." In an internal segment the cogs are on the inside so as to drive the pinion and jackshaft, etc., in the same direction that the water wheel turns.

Showing Silent Chain Drive direct from shaft of Fitz Water Wheel to line shaft from which the dynamo is driven. The water wheel here is the one shown on page 22. It is set on the outside of the building with the shaft extended thru the wall to carry the sprocket wheel. Morse Silent Chain is used for the drive and the generator is a slow speed D. C., 125 volt, Fairbanks. The plant is in continuous operation, but the motion of the water wheel is so smooth and steady that no governor is needed.

All our segment gearing, as well as other gearing furnished by us, is made of our own semi-steel mixture in our own foundry, specializing on this class of work. We have one of the largest stocks of gear patterns in the country available for water wheel work, and can furnish practically anything needed in this line. In segment gears alone we make over 400 sizes and are equally well equipped with independent spur gear and bevel gear patterns. Within the last year we have installed new machinery to saw and finish complete cogs for mortise gears and are prepared to furnish machine cut, ready-dressed cogs to the general public at very attractive prices.

On the following pages we show a number of plans such as we frequently use to connect up our water wheels to various classes of machinery in different locations. A study of these plans will be found of great assistance to any one who is planning to install a steel overshoot wheel in place of his existing equipment. However, these illustrations are only intended as suggestions to the customer, and we would prefer to make the final recommendations ourselves in each case after receiving the necessary data and suggestions.

Solid Spur Master Wheel made of semi-steel casting from our own formula and in our own foundry.

Internal Spur Master Wheel. Made solid, just like the external gear, but intended to drive pinion in same direction as the water wheel turns.

Old Pre-Revolutionary Paper Mill at Roslyn, L. I., once visited by George Washington, but abandoned years ago on account of supposed failure of water power. Now restored by Roslyn Neighborhood Association and used to light Roslyn Park by means of a Fitz Steel Overshoot.

The Fitz Wheel With Segment Gear

THE FITZ EQUIPPED WITH SEGMENT GEARING

We can furnish segment gears with the cogs on the outside of the circle as shown or on the inside of the circle just as desired. The latter type is known as an internal segment gear and will drive the pinion wheel in the same direction that the water wheel travels.

This illustration shows the simple and direct manner in which the Fitz Wheel can be connected up to fast-running machinery. The segment gear is probably more frequently used than any other plan for large diameter wheels, as it will fit almost any situation.

Fitz segment gears are about as different from ordinary segment gears as Fitz Water Wheels are from the old-style wood wheel. The gear castings are made of a mixture of cast iron and steel by a formula of our own. The steel alloy adds greatly to their strength and durability. The cogs of our gears are ground smooth, not by hand but by a special machine designed for that purpose. The ends of the segments also are now ground by machinery so as to have a full bearing against each other, and prevent any tendency to work loose. No factory lacking our special equipment can duplicate this process. By our method of construction, the side bolts are relieved from the strain of transmitting the power of the wheel. All segment bolts are equipped with patented grip nut locks and made to drive into the holes. See page 56 for detailed view.

The Fitz With Spur Master Wheel Drive

SPUR MASTER WHEEL ON END OF WATER WHEEL SHAFT

This style of gearing is the ideal one for every location in which it can be used. The master wheel is keyed to the water wheel shaft inside of the mill and is entirely separate from the water wheel itself. The master wheel may be either a spur gear as shown in the illustration, or a bevel gear to drive a shaft at right angles with the water wheel shaft. The spur gear is the best to use wherever circumstances will permit and we recommend that it be mounted on the extreme end of the water wheel shaft as shown in our cut.

Master wheels are made in any diameter wanted up to 16 ft. Those 8 ft. in diameter and smaller are generally made solid, altho they can be furnished split if necessary. From 9 to 12 ft. diameter inclusive, we furnish split wheels for convenience in transportation and installing in the mill. The larger sizes are built up in sections for the same reason.

The material used in our master wheel gears is semi-steel instead of ordinary cast iron. A patented locking device is used on the nuts of all split gears.

Master wheel drives are not quite as convenient to use with very large diameter wheels as they are with lower and medium diameter water wheels for the reason that they cannot be furnished in such large diameters as segment gears and hence do not drive the pinion shaft as fast. We recommend their use, however, wherever the conditions are suitable.

INTERNAL SEGMENT GEAR

Segment Gears are intended to bolt to the spokes of the water wheel, instead of being mounted independently on the water wheel shaft. They are made up in segments of a circle to correspond with the number of spokes in the water wheel, and can be provided in either external or internal types to suit the machinery that is to be driven.

Segment Gears are useful for transmitting power from water wheels of large diameter. Our gears are made of a special semi-steel alloy developed in our own foundry, and having much more strength than ordinary cast iron. Great care is used to prevent warping in moulding. The bolts used to assemble the segments are made up especially for our needs from an alloy steel that has three times the strength of ordinary steel bolts. The nuts are locked by patented lock-nuts (not lock washers) that hold them securely in place.

Not a bolt hole is drilled in our segment gear until the entire segment is fitted upon the water wheel itself, right in our shops. Then the segments are assembled in a true circle, and all holes are drilled thru the segments and arms of the wheel before taking apart for shipment. This makes a true, durable and easy-running gear.

EXTERNAL SEGMENT GEAR

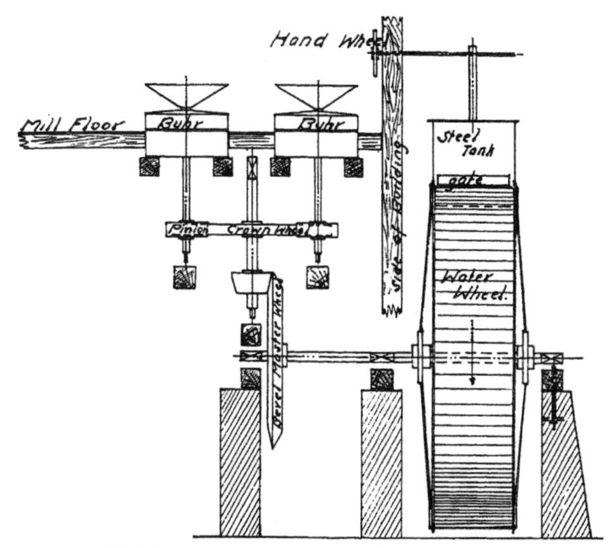

THE FITZ WITH BEVEL MASTER WHEEL
TO DRIVE BUHRS

This is one of our popular plans for driving old mills where a wood wheel was once used. The old gear wheel can be used again by an ingenious method we have of filling up the eye to suit our steel shaft. An old spur gear can be used the same way.

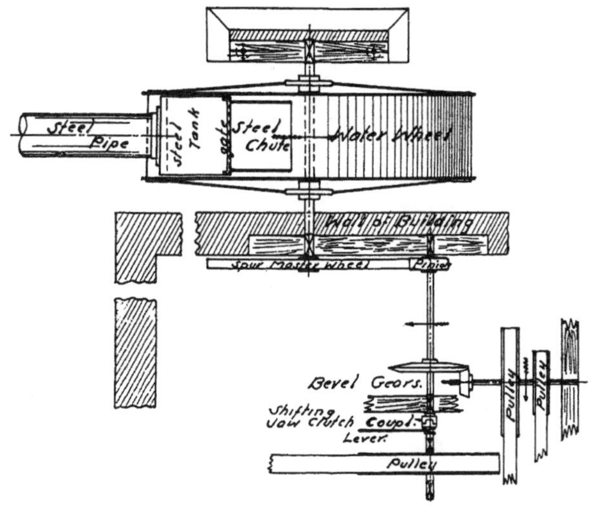

THE FITZ WITH SPUR MASTER WHEEL TO
DRIVE ROLLER MILL AND BUHRS

A Spur Gear is used here instead of a bevel gear as in the other cut. The Roll line shaft can be driven from a large pulley on the jackshaft. The buhrs are driven from pulleys mounted on the upright shaft. Either the buhrs or the roller mill can be disconnected easily when desired.

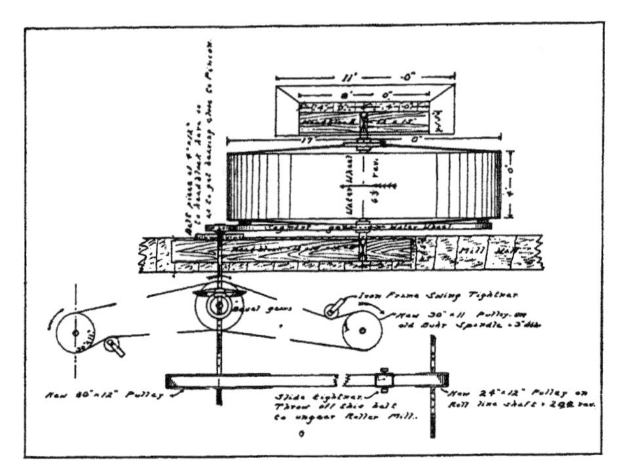

THE FITZ WITH SEGMENT GEAR DRIVING A FLOUR MILL AND BUHRS

This plan is frequently used in mills where a turbine was formerly installed or where the floors are too low to allow a master wheel to be used.

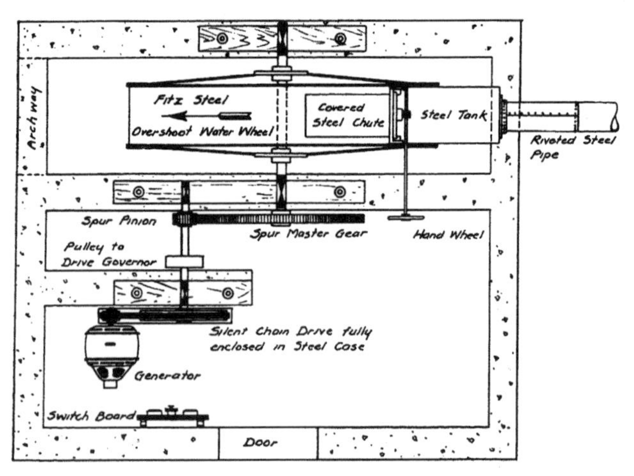

Design for small hydro-electric plant, using machine cut spur master wheel and Morse Silent Chain Drive to one of our special slow speed generators.

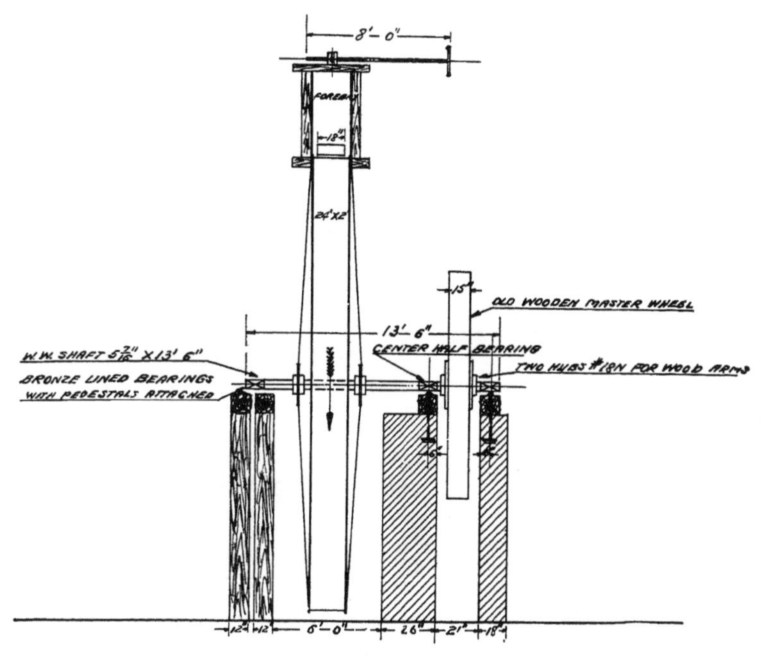

USING AN OLD WOOD MASTER WHEEL

In displacing a wood overshoot wheel, in cases where the old master wheel is still in good condition, we can arrange to use it again on our steel shaft by means of a special flange or octagon bush or pair of flanges as shown.

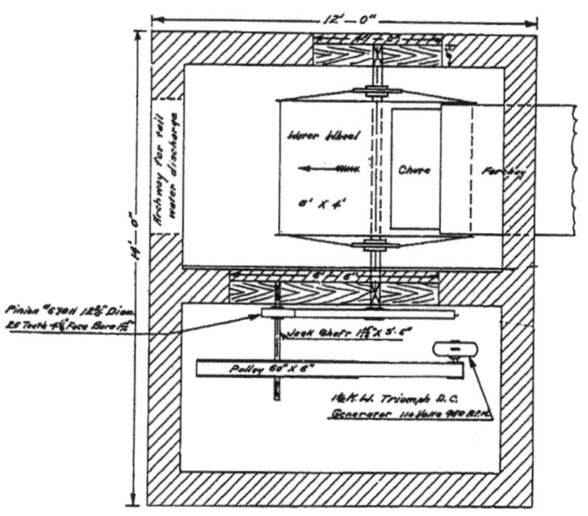

FITZ WITH SPUR MASTER WHEEL AND BELT DRIVE DIRECT TO SLOW SPEED GENERATOR

The Steel Overshoot affords an ideal source of power for electrical energy. Slow Speed Generators suitable for this drive are now available in all sizes.

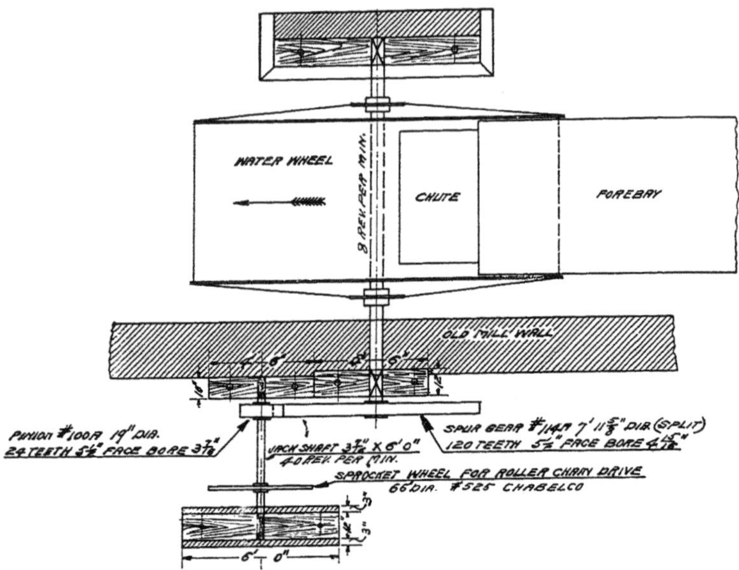

WATER WHEEL WITH MASTER WHEEL AND ROLLER CHAIN DRIVE

In some locations the space is too limited for a belt drive and yet the line shaft is too far away to use a gear drive from the jackshaft. A roller chain drive is used here to overcome this difficulty. The roller chain runs just like a belt without reversing the motion of the driven shaft.

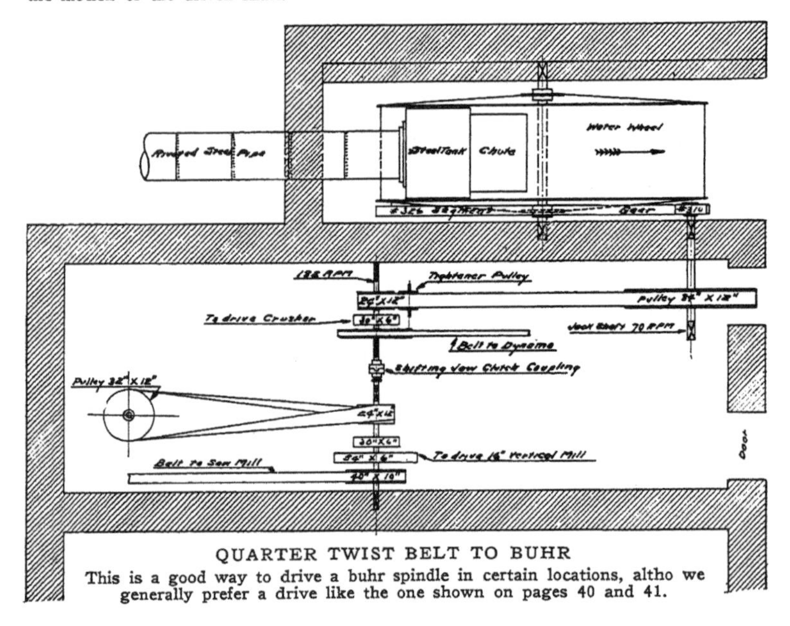

QUARTER TWIST BELT TO BUHR

This is a good way to drive a buhr spindle in certain locations, altho we generally prefer a drive like the one shown on pages 40 and 41.

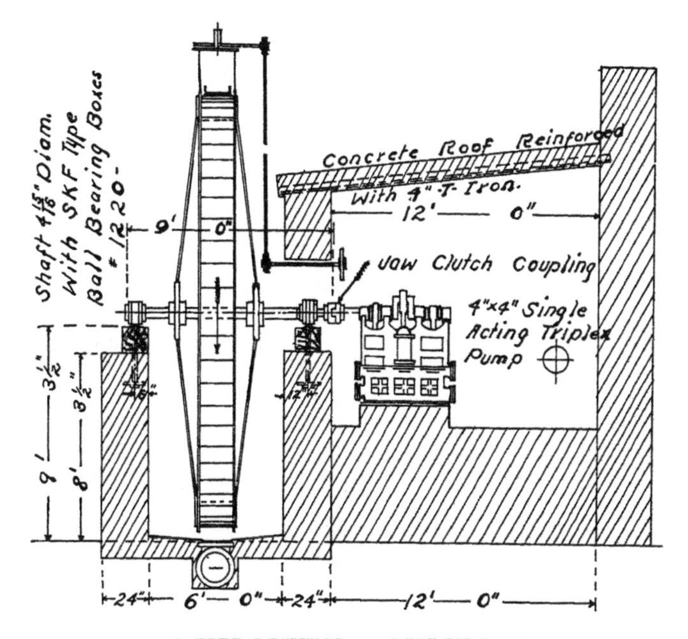

A FITZ DRIVING A TRIPLEX PUMP

This plan is often used for Municipal Water Works or for any situation where very heavy pressure is encountered.

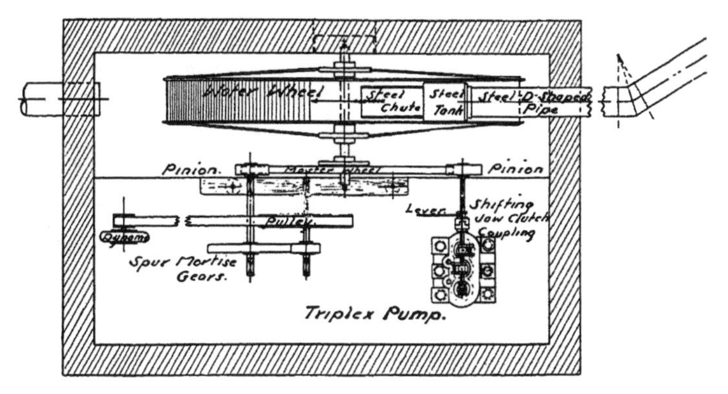

A COMBINATION PUMPING AND ELECTRIC LIGHT PLANT DRIVEN BY THE FITZ

The dynamo here is an old-style high speed machine requiring double gearing to the countershaft to get the necessary velocity. Several builders are now putting out slow speed generators especially designed for this class of work, that can be readily driven from a single pulley mounted on our jackshaft. See page 42 (lower plan).

Terms and Prices

There being so many sizes and conditions under which these wheels must work, it is impossible to have a printed price list for them. Each wheel is built to suit its own particular location and each job is estimated on separately. Give us the information asked for below and we will be enabled to quote you on just what you need for your location.

All prices quoted are on a basis of net cash. However, when good security is given, and our customers desire it, we can accept half or one-third cash and balance in three, six, nine or twelve months' negotiable notes bearing interest at six per cent, this being the same as cash to us, for we can have notes discounted at face value when necessary. Of course, this applies only to customers living within the United States and secured by good endorsers. To all others, our terms are strictly net cash on delivery at New York.

All parts are plainly marked or numbered and are very easy to put together, having been previously fitted together in our shops. If desired, we will furnish free with each wheel a blue-print drawing for installation, with necessary tools and full instructions for putting together.

Data Needed for Estimates

In order to make an intelligent estimate on what you need, we must know something about the situation where the wheel is to go. When writing for prices, please give us, if possible, the number of cubic feet of water per minute that your stream will flow at ordinary times, measured by one of the methods described in this booklet. If not convenient to do this, let us know what size and make of wheel you are now using and how much work you can now do with it.

Also give the total fall you have from the top of the head water in the forebay to the surface of the standing water in the tail race.

Give speed of line shaft, etc., to be driven by the wheel.

Tell us how your present wheel is geared to run your machinery, and if you can do so, send us a rough sketch of the same.

State whether you are troubled by back water and give any other in formation you think may have any bearing on the situation.

Measurement of Water

It is highly important to those who contemplate improving or utilizing their water power to determine the head that can be secured—that is, the vertical distance from the surface of tail-water to the surface of head-water. Then ascertain the amount of water that can be relied upon. It would not be prudent for parties to subject themselves to an expense without having the assurance of having power sufficient to propel their proposed machinery. It has frequently occurred that mills and factories have been completed, and not until then the mistake discovered.

By knowing the head and number of cubic feet of water that flows per minute, the size of wheel that is best adapted can be selected and the horsepower determined. We would, therefore, recommend, when convenient, to get some one who is skilled in hydraulics to make the calculations; however, if this cannot be conveniently done, parties can measure their streams themselves by methods which we propose.

There are many ways by which streams of water can be measured approximately, but, undoubtedly, the most correct way by which it can be done, is by means of a "Weir Dam," as shown on page 64. If the stream is too large, take a board, or, if required, joint and nail together with cleats more than one, wide and long enough to form a dam across the stream. Cut a notch in the top of the board of sufficient depth to allow all the water to pass through. The length of said notch should not be more than half or two-thirds the width of dam, and should be beveled on the down side of the stream nearly to a feathered edge. Be particular to have the notch level across the stream so the water will be of the same depth at both ends. Drive a stake in the ground about four feet up the stream from the board, so that the top of the stake will be on a level with the bottom of said notch, which can readily be seen when the water begins to flow over it.

When the dam is made perfectly tight, so that all the water passes through the notch or Weir, and the water raised to its maximum height, measure carefully how much the water raises above the top of stake. This measurement is the basis from which the calculations are made to find the amount of water that flows per minute, as shown in the Weir Table on page 65. Care must be taken to get a board wide enough to dam the water to a dead level before it begins to flow over the notch, and that the water has a fall, enough to clear itself below—say a depth of six inches, or more in a large stream.

Another matter of importance is the possibility of storing the water by means of a dam or pond, so that the machinery can be run during the time when the regular flow of the stream is not sufficient—say, if the location admits, a dam or pond can be constructed so as to store the water through the night to be used through the day, or store and use as the case may suit; thus, if the water can be stored for twelve hours, the next twelve the power will be double that of the regular stream.

We emphatically state that every water power in existence within the range of this type of wheel can be greatly improved by the use of our Fitz Steel Overshoot Water Wheel. No difference whose make or what kind of a wheel is used, we can increase your power 25% to 50%. This is especially true of light streams, where the economical use of water is an object.

SHOWING WEIR DAM AND MEASUREMENT OF WATER

THE WEIR TABLE

	0	1/8	1/4	3/8	1/2	5/8	3/4	7/8
0	.00	.01	.05	.09	.14	.19	.26	.32
1	.40	.47	.55	.64	.73	.82	.92	1.02
2	1.13	1.23	1.35	1.46	1.58	1.70	1.82	1.95
3	2.07	2.21	2.34	2.48	2.61	2.76	2.90	3.05
4	3.20	3.35	3.50	3.66	3.81	3.97	4.14	4.30
5	4.47	4.64	4.81	4.98	5.15	5.33	5.51	5.69
6	5.87	6.06	6.25	6.44	6.62	6.82	7.01	7.21
7	7.40	7.60	7.80	8.01	8.21	8.42	8.63	8.83
8	9.05	9.26	9.47	9.69	9.91	10.13	10.35	10.57
9	10.80	11.03	11.25	11.48	11.71	11.94	12.17	12.41
10	12.64	12.88	13.12	13.36	13.60	13.85	14.09	14.34
11	14.59	14.84	15.09	15.34	15.59	15.85	16.11	16.36
12	16.62	16.88	17.15	17.41	17.67	17.94	18.21	18.47
13	18.74	19.01	19.29	19.56	19.84	20.11	20.39	20.67
14	20.95	21.23	21.51	21.80	22.08	22.37	22.65	22.94
15	23.23	23.52	23.82	24.11	24.40	24.70	25.00	25.30
16	25.60	25.90	26.20	26.50	26 80	27.11	27.42	27.72
17	28.03	28.34	28.65	28.97	29.28	29.59	29.91	30.22
18	30.54	30.86	31.18	31.50	31.82	32.15	32.47	32.80
19	33.12	33.45	33.78	34.11	34.44	34.77	35.10	35.44
20	35.77	36.11	36.45	36.78	37.12	37.46	37.80	38.15
21	38.49	38.83	39.18	39.53	39.87	40.22	40.57	40.92
22	41.27	41.62	41.98	42.33	42.69	43.04	43.40	43.76
23	44.12	44.48	44.84	45.20	45.56	45.93	46.29	46.66
24	47.03	47.39	47.76	48.13	48.50	48.87	49.24	49.62

This table is to assist in ascertaining the capacity of a stream of water. It gives the number of cubic feet of water that will pass over a Weir one inch wide, and from 1/8 of an inch to 2 7/8 in depth. The figures on the first upright column represent whole inches, and those on the top horizontal line represent fractional parts of an inch of depth over the Weir. The figures on the second upright column indicate the number of cubic feet of water that will flow per minute over the Weir, for whole inches in depth, and on the succeeding columns whole inches and the fractions under which they occur. Then the number of cubic feet thus found, multiplied by the width of the Weir in inches, will give the capacity of a stream.

EXAMPLE:—To find the required number of cubic feet of water that will flow over a Weir, 6½ inches in depth and 50 inches in width, follow down the left hand column of figures in the table to 6, then across, until directly under the ½ in the top line, where will be found 6.62; this, multiplied by 50, will give 331, the number of cubic feet of water that passes over the whole Weir.

MEASUREMENT OF LARGER STREAMS

In streams too large to measure by Weir, the Float Measurement method may be used. Select a place where the bed of the stream is smooth and comparatively uniform both as to width and as to depth. Throw into the middle of the stream some light floating objects of sufficient weight to sink well into the water. Time the passage of these floats between certain fixed points, say 20 or 30 ft. apart. The average velocity of the stream will be about 75% of the velocity of the floats, for the water does not run as fast along the sides or on the bed of the stream as it does in the center of the stream.

Secure the average depth and average width of the stream at the points where the velocity was taken. The more nearly uniform the stream is in width and depth, the nearer correct your estimates will be. Multiply the average depth (in feet) by the average width (in feet), and multiply the product by the velocity in feet per minute as ascertained from the floats. The result will be the number of cubic feet per minute which the stream flows.

MEASUREMENT OF WATER THROUGH OPENINGS UNDER PRESSURE

Table giving the number of cubic feet of water discharged per minute, by an orifice one inch square, under any head from 3 to 62 in.

Head	Cubic Feet	Head	Cubic Feet	Head	Cubic Feet	Head	Cubic Feet	Head	Cubic Feet	Head	Cubic Feet
3	1.12	13	2.20	23	2.91	33	3.47	43	3.95	53	4.39
4	1.27	14	2.27	24	2 97	34	3.52	44	4 00	54	4.42
5	1.41	15	2.36	25	3.03	35	3.57	45	4.05	55	4.46
6	1.53	16	2.44	26	3.09	36	3.63	46	4.10	56	4.52
7	1.64	17	2.51	27	3.15	37	3.67	47	4.13	57	4.55
8	1.75	18	2.58	28	3.20	38	3.72	48	4.18	58	4.58
9	1.85	19	2.65	29	3.26	39	3.77	49	4.22	59	4.63
10	1.94	20	2.72	30	3.32	40	3.82	50	4.27	60	4.66
11	2.03	21	2.78	31	3.37	41	3.86	51	4.30	61	4.72
12	2.12	22	2.85	32	3.42	42	3.92	52	4.34	62	4.74

Suppose the opening to let the water on an overshoot wheel be 36 inches long and the gate hoisted two inches; the head of water above the opening, 25 inches. Multiply the length, 36, by 2 (the height the gate is hoisted), and the result will be 72, the number of square inches in opening.

By referring to the foregoing table, opposite 25 inch head will be found 3.03; this, multiplied by 72, gives 218.16, the number of cubic feet of water discharged per minute.

MEASUREMENTS IN MINER'S INCHES

A miner's inch is the quantity of water that will flow through an orifice one inch square when the head above the center of the orifice is six inches. This is but an approximate definition, as the "miner's inch" seems to be differently understood in different sections. It ranges in value from 1.20 to 1.76 cubic feet per minute, but with a head of six inches is about 1.60 cubic feet per minute.

When correspondents speak of miner's inches they should accompany their statement by a description of the kind of miner's inch they have in view, when writing. As we have before intimated, the amount of pressure over the opening differs in different parts of the country, or in different mining districts, and each depth, or miner's inch, will discharge differently. The kind of miner's inch we have described above, is one that is generally used.

A miner's inch is a measure for flow of water, and is an opening one inch square in plank, two inches thick, under a head of six inches of water to upper edge of opening.

TO COMPUTE HORSE-POWER

A horse-power is the amount of power required to raise 33,000 pounds one foot per minute. To compute the horse-power of any stream, multiply the number of cubic feet of water it flows per minute by 62⅓ (which is the weight in pounds of one cubic foot). Multiply that product by the head (in feet) and divide the product by 33,000. The quotient will be the full horse-power of the stream.

Most turbine manufacturers claim that their wheels will develop 80% efficiency, but it is well known that very few of them in actual use will ever reach 70% efficiency, and then only under the most favorable conditions.

The Fitz will develop from 90% to 95% efficiency, depending upon the diameter of the wheel; or at least one-third more power than any other wheel using the same amount of water. It will develop just as high efficiency at one-third or one-fourth capacity as it will when run at normal capacity. A turbine will do practically no work at all when run much below full gate, so that in the course of a year's run on a variable stream, the Fitz will develop twice the power of the most economical turbine.

Water Wheel Definitions

SPUR GEAR

The EFFICIENCY of a water wheel is the actual horse-power which it develops with a certain amount of water as compared with the power which it is theoretically possible to develop with that amount of water. It is impossible to develop the full theoretical power, for there must always be some loss, but the nearer a wheel approaches this performance, the higher the efficiency. Thus when you have calculated the horse-power a stream affords by one of the methods we have described, you can depend on nearly 95% of this power if a Fitz is used, or only 60% to 70% if a turbine or wood wheel is used. This difference in efficiency becomes much greater when it is necessary to run at part gate or after the wheel has been used a few years.

BACK-WATER occurs when the tail race from the mill becomes clogged or choked so that the wheel has to wade in the water it discharges. The greatest care should be exercised to avoid this condition.

The JACKSHAFT is the shaft which carries the pinion wheel which gears into the segment gear, or master wheel.

The SEGMENT, or SEGMENT GEAR, as the name indicates, is a gear wheel composed of a number of pieces which are segments of a circle. It is bolted to the arms or housings of the water wheel. The segment gear, as we make it, is quite a different thing from the rude and troublesome device employed on the old wood wheels. (See pages 17, 18, 54 and 56 for illustration.)

BEVEL GEAR

A PINION is a small gear wheel which gears into a larger one.

The MAIN DRIVE PULLEY is the large pulley or belt wheel that usually goes on our jackshaft and carries the belt that drives the line shaft to proper speed.

Definitions—Continued

The CHUTE is the short trough of wood or iron which conveys the water from the gate to the buckets of the water wheel. It is generally about three feet long.

Spur Master Wheel. We make these of our own semi-steel formula. Can furnish either solid or split.

A Master Wheel is a large cog wheel that is keyed to the water wheel shaft instead of being bolted to the arms of the water wheel like a segment gear. It can be furnished either in the spur gear type as shown herewith or in the bevel gear type with cogs like those in the upper cut on page 57.

The "Tight Iron Gate" that we furnish with our water wheels is an iron regulating gate to control the amount of water admitted to the water wheel and to cut off the delivery of water when the wheel is to be stopped. It is made of cast iron and is simple in design and construction, but we use the greatest possible care in machining it. A good tight gate is of very great importance in securing the utmost economy in the use of water, and we believe our gate fulfils every requirement in this respect.

The accompanying illustrations show our iron gate just as we furnish

IRON GATE WITH CUT-OFF SLAB REMOVED

it with our water wheels in standard practice. It may be mounted by the customer in a wood forebay as shown in the illustration on pages 7, 33, and others in this catalog; or in a concrete forebay as shown on page 71. Or a still better plan is to have us mount the gate here at the factory in a steel tank or box such as we show on pages 18, 20, 36, 37, and at many other points in our catalog. The steel tank is especially convenient in cases where the water is carried to the wheel thru iron pipe, as it affords the best method of connection and, of course, it is always the easiest and quickest to install. It is never furnished, however, except at an extra price, and should be expressly specified in the contract.

GATE CLOSED

STEEL TANKS AND PIPE

Our steel tanks are almost as far ahead of the old-style wood forebay as the Fitz is ahead of the wood wheel. Iron pipe is used to convey the water from the dam or race way to the tank, from which it is discharged to the wheel through our water-tight iron gate, thus making a complete and permanent water-tight job. This method of conveying the water is immensely more satisfactory than the use of dirt raceways, which are always breaking out, and wood flumes, which are always rotting. In many cases, too, even the first cost is less than that of the leaky wood flumes.

Our Drop End Tanks

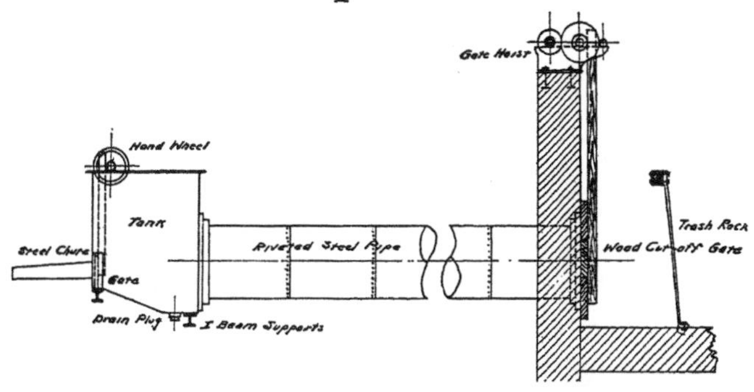

Our Drop End Steel Tanks have been developed for the purpose of saving our customers the expense of using the higher priced D-shaped pipe on long flume lines and yet to enable them to secure the same advantages of preserving full capacity and conserving the full head available. This is accomplished by our plan of depressing the rear end of the tank as shown above to enable the center line of the pipe to be laid at about the level of top of the water wheel buckets. By this method practically the full area of the pipe is always available for the water to flow thru and the wheel cannot be "starved" thru the contraction of the pipe area.

A Drop End Tank necessarily costs more than a level-bottom tank such as we show on page 70, but in a flume of more than 25 ft. length this extra cost is considerably over-balanced by the saving in the cost of the round-pipe as compared with D-Shaped Pipe. Examples of Drop-End Tanks may be seen in the illustrations on pages 71, 72 and others in this catalog.

FITZ IRON GATE IN CONCRETE FOREBAY

This illustration shows one of our iron gates mounted in place in a concrete forebay at Parnell Tavern, St. Thomas, Pa. Note how tight the gate shuts off the water, altho this photo was taken ten years after installation.

Round Riveted Steel Flume and our new style Dropped End Steel Tank to feed water wheel. This type of tank or gate box permits the use of round feed pipe without sacrifice of head, thus affording an economical water-tight all-steel flume.

Riveted Steel Water Pipe

The use of steel pipe in place of wood forebays originated in California, where it is extremely popular. The rest of the country is now rapidly recognizing its value. The cost of steel pipe is considerably more than terra cotta, but it is so much cheaper to install that the final cost is almost the same. Unlike terra cotta, it will stand almost any amount of pressure and can follow the lay of the ground instead of having to have a straight ditch dug for it. It is more durable, will not leak, and is not liable to breakage.

Price List of Riveted Pipe

Painted inside and out. No flanges included

Diameter of Pipe in inches	Thickness by Stubbs gauge	Equivalent in inches	Price per lineal foot	Diameter of Pipe in inches	Thickness by Stubbs gauge	Equivalent in inches	Price per lineal foot
12	No. 14	$\frac{5}{64}$	$2.65	22	No. 7	$\frac{3}{16}$	$7.00
14	14	$\frac{5}{64}$	3.00	24	14	$\frac{5}{64}$	4.40
14	12	$\frac{7}{64}$	3.35	24	12	$\frac{7}{64}$	5.00
14	10	$\frac{9}{64}$	3.75	24	10	$\frac{9}{64}$	5.70
16	14	$\frac{5}{64}$	3.25	24	8	$\frac{11}{64}$	6.50
16	12	$\frac{7}{64}$	3.75	24	7	$\frac{3}{16}$	7.50
16	10	$\frac{9}{64}$	4.30	30	14	$\frac{5}{64}$	4.90
16	8	$\frac{11}{64}$	5.00	30	12	$\frac{7}{64}$	5.50
18	14	$\frac{5}{64}$	3.60	30	10	$\frac{9}{64}$	6.30
18	12	$\frac{7}{64}$	4.10	30	8	$\frac{11}{64}$	7.00
18	10	$\frac{9}{64}$	4.50	30	7	$\frac{3}{16}$	8.00
18	8	$\frac{11}{64}$	5.25	36	12	$\frac{7}{64}$	6.95
20	14	$\frac{5}{64}$	3.75	36	10	$\frac{9}{64}$	7.65
20	12	$\frac{7}{64}$	4.25	36	8	$\frac{11}{64}$	8.50
20	10	$\frac{9}{64}$	4.85	36	7	$\frac{3}{16}$	9.50
20	8	$\frac{11}{64}$	5.40	42	8	$\frac{11}{64}$	9.80
22	14	$\frac{5}{64}$	4.10	42	7	$\frac{3}{16}$	10.90
22	12	$\frac{7}{64}$	4.60	48	7	$\frac{3}{16}$	12.50
22	10	$\frac{9}{64}$	5.25	54	7	$\frac{3}{16}$	14.00
22	8	$\frac{11}{64}$	6.00	54	3	$\frac{1}{4}$	17.75

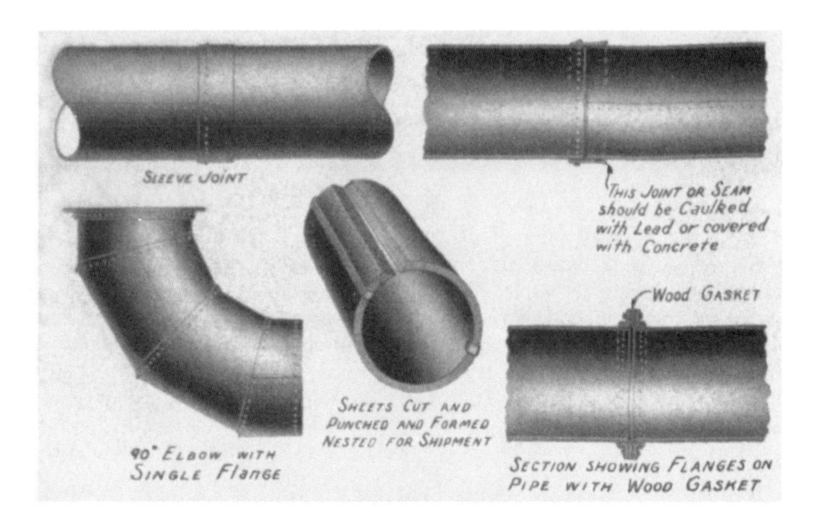

Where the flume pipe can be laid right on the ground or in a trench, the Fitz Sleeve Joint affords the best and most economical means of assembling the various sections of pipe. This design was originated by our firm and is exclusive with us. For overhead work, the flange joint should be used. For export shipments the pipe can be knocked down and nested to occupy a very small space.

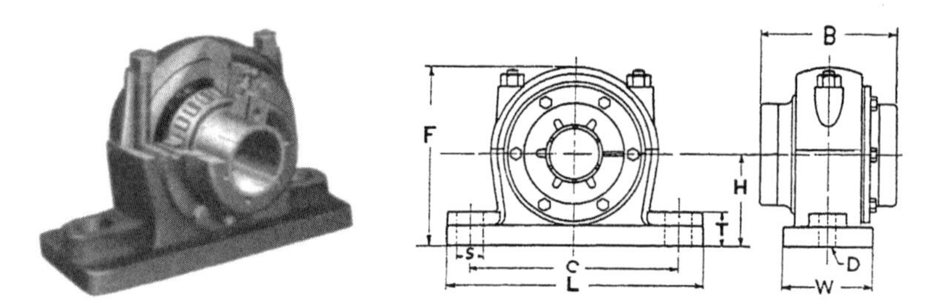

TIMKEN ROLLER BEARING PILLOW BLOCKS (SELF-ALIGNING)

Shaft	B	H	L	W	T	C	D Bolt	S	F	Price
1 7/16"	5½	3	9	3¼	1⅛	7	½	1	5¾	$21.00
1 11/16"	5¾	3¼	9½	3½	1¼	7½	½	1	6¼	24.00
1 15/16"	6	3½	10½	3¾	1⅜	8¼	⅝	1⅛	6¾	26.00
2 3/16"	6¼	3⅞	11¼	4	1½	9	⅝	1⅛	7½	30.00
2 7/16"	6½	4⅛	12½	4¼	1⅝	10	¾	1⅜	8	36.00
2 11/16"	7⅜	4¾	13½	4¾	1¾	11	¾	1⅜	9¼	48.00
2 15/16"	7⅜	4¾	13½	4¾	1¾	11	¾	1⅜	9¼	48.00
3 7/16"	7¾	5¼	15	5¼	1⅞	12	⅞	1⅝	10¼	70.00
3 15/16"	9	6¼	18	6¼	2¼	14½	⅞	1¾	12¼	150.00
4 7/16"	10	7	19½	7	2¾	16	⅞	1¾	13¾	220.00
4 15/16"	11½	8	23	8	3	19	1	2	15⅞	400.00

SINGLE-GEARED GATE HOIST

An inexpensive outfit which saves much time and labor for the water power user.

FITZ DOUBLE-GEARED GATE HOIST

This hoist is suitable for larger and heavier gates than the other two. It is a very powerful and convenient hoist and will suit any ordinary situation. We also make a triple-geared hoist mounted on a cast frame like this, for still heavier service.

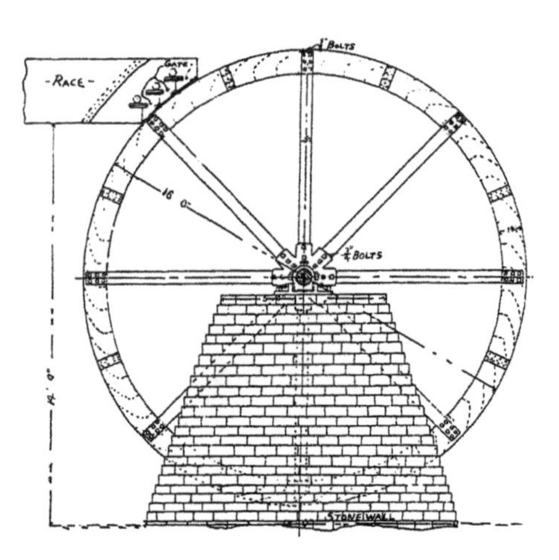

THE FITZ STEEL PITCH BACK WHEEL

The pitch back type of wheel is useful for certain situations where the fall is too low for an overshoot and there is too little water for a turbine. For situations where a pitch back is needed, we build the wheel as it should be built.

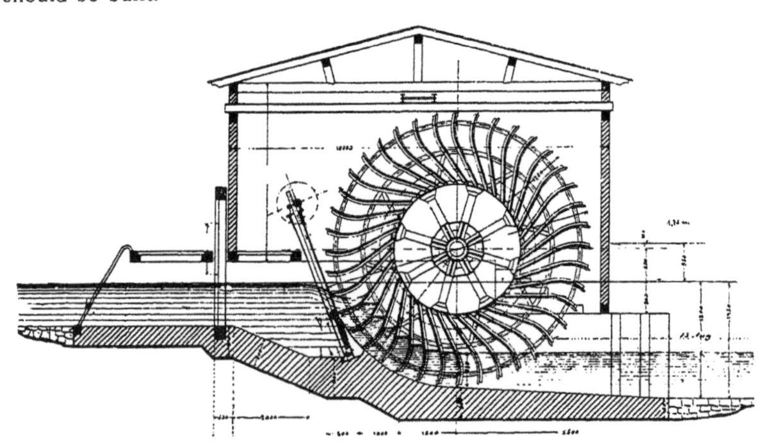

THE STEEL PONCELOT WHEEL

Where the fall is too low for any other type of water wheel, the Poncelot Wheel may be used with great success. Our Poncelot Design is in accordance with the best engineering principles and the wheel is built with the same skill and care that we devote to the Overshoot. We are glad to have an opportunity to furnish advice and estimates for the development of any water power.

FITZ UNDERSHOT WATER WHEEL

Wheels of this type can be used on very low falls to drive pumping plants. The illustration shows a plant built for Mr. W. C. Stephens, Carlisle, Pa., Route Six. This pumps water for a large dairy farm.

This little 6 ft. diameter Fitz Overshoot, using a total head of 8 ft., is pumping water to an elevation of nearly 350 ft.

Price List of Finished Shafting

Diameter	Weight per foot	Price	Diameter	Weight per foot	Price
1 7/16	5.47	$0.57	3 11/16	35.60	$3.67
1 11/16	7.58	.72	3 15/16	40.59	4.20
1 15/16	10.00	.93	4 3/16	45.00	5.25
2 3/16	12.75	1.20	4 7/16	51.55	5.92
2 7/16	16.00	1.50	4 15/16	63.82	7.20
2 11/16	18.98	1.87	5 7/16	77.40	10.50
2 15/16	23.00	2.13	5 15/16	91.20	13.35
3 3/16	26.95	2.65	6 7/16	108.05	16.87
3 7/16	31.56	3.25	6 15/16	126.00	21.00

Subject to discounts. Larger sizes at Special Rates.

The diameter of Shafting conforms to Standard gauge and any deviation therefrom will be charged extra.

Boxing extra, at cost. Not responsible for safe and prompt delivery after shipment.

In ordering shafting give size, length and place of journals and key ways.

RULES TO DETERMINE THE SIZE AND SPEED OF PULLEYS AND GEARS

The driving pulley is called the "Driver," and the driven pulley the "Driven." If the number of teeth is used in gears instead of the diameter, merely substitute "number of teeth" where "diameter" occurs in following rules:

To find the diameter of Driver: Multiply the diameter of the "Driven" by its revolutions and divide the product by the revolutions of the "Driver." The quotient will give the diameter of the "Driver."

To find the diameter of the Driven: Multiply the diameter of the "Driver" by its revolutions, and divide the product by the revolutions of the "Driven." The quotient will be the diameter of the "Driven."

To find the revolutions of the Driver: Multiply the diameter of the "Driven" by its revolutions and divide the product by the diameter of the "Driver." The quotient will be the revolutions of the "Driver."

To find the revolutions of the Driven: Multiply the diameter of the "Driver" by its revolutions, and divide the product by the diameter of the "Driven." The quotient will be revolutions of the "Driven."

Our Bronze Lined Self-Oiling Bearings are an important feature of Fitz Water Wheels. This is the type now furnished as standard equipment with all our water wheels except the very smallest sizes.

Instead of being babbitted, these bearings contain a heavy cast shell of Phosphor Bronze carefully fitted to the cast iron box. Then the complete journal box is put in a special boring lathe built for that purpose and bored out true and smooth. Suitable channels for oil are cut in the bronze and the cap is then fitted with a wick oiling device that keeps the shaft constantly lubricated.

The friction is very slight in our smooth bored bronze shells, and the durability is all that could be desired. Even in cases of the worst neglect, if the bearing should become cut or damaged, the old bronze liner can readily be slipped out of the journal and a new one put in its place without any of the usual loss of time.

Price List of Self-Oiling Bronze Lined Bearings

Size of Shaft	Length of Bearing	Distance from Centre of shaft to bottom of pedestal	Price
8 7/16"	18 1/4"	8 5/8" Sep. Ped.	$120.00
7 15/16"	17"	8 3/8" " "	95.00
7 7/16"	17"	8 1/8" " "	85.00
6 15/16"	15"	7 3/4" " "	80.00
6 7/16"	15"	7" " "	75.00
6 7/16"	12"	7" " "	65.00
5 15/16"	12"	6 3/8" " "	45.00
5 7/16"	12"	6" " "	40.00
4 15/16"	12"	5 7/8" " "	37.00
4 7/16"	11"	5 3/4" " "	34.00
3 15/16"	11"	4 3/8" Ped. att.	24.00

Hydraulic Information

One cubic foot of water.................................. 62.378 lbs.
One cubic inch of water.................................. 0.36 lbs.
One gallon of water.. 8.338 lbs.
One gallon of water..231. cu. in.
One cubic foot of water.................................. 7.476 gal.
One pound of water.. 27.7 cu. in.

Water falling is actuated by the same laws as falling bodies; passing through 1 foot in ¼ of a second, 4 feet in ½ of a second, 9 feet in ¾ of a second, and so on. Hence its velocity in flowing through an aperture in the side of a reservoir, bulkhead, or any vessel, is the same as a heavy body falling freely from a height equal to the distance from the middle of the aperture to the surface of the water.

To find the loss of head by water entering a pipe in which the mouthpiece is straight, multiply the square of the velocity by .0076 and the product will be the approximate loss in feet.

The loss of head by friction in a pipe increases directly with the length, with the square of the velocity, and with the roughness of the pipe. It decreases as the diameter of the pipe increases and is independent of the pressure or head of water.

To find the loss in feet:—Divide the product of the length and the square of the velocity in feet per second by the diameter in inches and then multiply this quotient by 0.0056 for pipes up to 6 inches diameter; by 0.0047 for pipes between 6 inches and 21 inches in diameter; by 0.0037 for pipes between 21 and 48 inches diameter; by 0.0028 for pipes between 48 inches and 72 inches diameter, and by 0.0019 for pipes larger than 72 inches diameter. This formula will give approximate results within at least 10% of correctness for smooth straight pipe.

Roughly speaking, the loss of head in 100 feet of pipe is equivalent to one-half the velocity squared, divided by the diameter of the pipe in inches.

To find the friction head necessary to give a required velocity in an open flume or canal: Multiply 0.001 the length in feet by the square of the velocity in feet per second, and by the sum of the two side measurements, the bottom width and one-tenth the top width; and finally divide the product thus obtained by the number of square feet in the section of the stream, and this quotient will be the loss of head in the stream in question.

One acre-foot equals 12 acre-inches, equals 43,560 cubic feet, equals 325,829 gallons.

A flow of one second-foot will produce one acre-inch in about an hour.

One pound per square inch pressure is equivalent to the pressure of a column of water 2.31 feet in height.

A column of water one foot in height produces a pressure of .433 pounds per square inch.

Gearing

The following table shows the greatest horsepower which different kinds of gears of one inch pitch and one inch face will safely transmit at various pitch line velocities. To find the greatest horse-power which any other pitch and face will safely transmit, the following rule can be used:

Rule 5.—Given——the pitch (in inches), face (in inches), velocity of pitch circle (in feet per second), and kind of gear; to find——the greatest horse-power that can be safely transmitted.

First find the horse-power in the table which the given kind of wheel with one inch pitch and one inch face will safely transmit at the given velocity.

Second—Multiply the pitch by the face.

Third—Multiply the horse-power found, by the product of pitch by face.

The final product is the horse-power required.

Table Showing the Horse-power which Different Kinds of Gear Wheels of One Inch Pitch and One Inch Face Will Transmit at Various Velocities of Pitch Circle.

1	2	3	4	5
Velocity of Pitch Circle in Feet per Second	Spur Wheels	Spur Mortise Wheels	Bevel Wheels	Wheels Bevel Mortise
2	1.338	.647	.938	.647
3	1.756	.971	1.227	.856
6	2.782	1.76	1.76	1.363
12	4.43	3.1	3.1	2.16
18	5.793	4.058	4.058	2.847
24	7.025	4.931	4.931	3.447
30	8.182	5.727	5.727	4.036
36	9.163	6.414	6.414	4.516
42	10.156	7.102	7.102	4.963
48	11.083	7.680	7.680	5.411

Rules for Calculating Length of Belting Before Pulleys are Placed in Position

Add together the diameter of the two pulleys and multiply the sum by 3.14159. To half of the result thus obtained add twice the distance from center of one pulley (or shaft) to center of the other pulley (or shaft).

Example:—Given the distance between centers of pulleys, 28 feet 8 inches; diameter of pulleys, 52 inches and 46 inches. What is length of Belt?

$$52+46=98\times3.14159=307.87 \text{ inches.}$$
$$307.8\div2=153.98 \text{ inches}\div12=12.83 \text{ feet.}$$
$$\text{Centres } 28\tfrac{8}{12} \text{ feet}\times2= \quad 57.33 \text{ “}$$

Answer $70\tfrac{1}{6}$ feet.

TIGHTENERS:—The tightening pulley is applied to the belt to increase its adhesion to the pulley, and as this is to fall first on the smaller pulley, it is usual to place it on the slack side of the belt near this pulley in order to increase the area of contact as well as adhesion. It also increases the friction of driving in proportion to the thrusting of the belt from the line of its natural curvature.

HORSE-POWER TRANSMITTED BY LEATHER BELTS

SINGLE BELTS

N. B.—Belts supposed to be not overstrained, so they will last.
1 inch wide, 800 feet per minute—1 Horse power

Speed in feet per minute	WIDTH OF BELT IN INCHES											
	2	3	4	5	6	8	10	12	14	16	18	20
	H.P.	H.P.	H.P.	H.P.	H.P.	H.P.	H.P.	H.P.	H.P.	H.P.	H.P.	H.P.
400	1	1½	2	2½	3	4	5	6	7	8	9	10
600	1½	2¼	3	3¾	4½	6	7½	9	10½	12	13½	15
800	2	3	4	5	6	8	10	12	14	16	18	20
1000	2½	3¼	5	6¼	7½	10	12½	15	17½	20	22½	25
1200	3	4½	6	7½	9	12	15	18	21	24	27	30
1500	3¾	5¾	7½	9½	11½	15	18¾	22½	26½	30	33¾	37½
1800	4½	6¾	9	11¼	13½	18	22½	27	31½	36	40½	45
2000	5	7½	10	12½	15	20	25	30	35	40	45	50
2400	6	9	12	15	18	24	30	36	42	48	54	60
2800	7	10½	14	17½	21	28	35	42	49	56	63	70
3000	7½	11¼	15	18¾	22½	30	37½	45	52½	60	67½	75
3500	8¾	13	17½	22	26	35	44	52½	61	70	79	88
4000	10	15	20	25	30	40	50	60	70	80	90	100
4500	11¼	17	22½	28	34	45	57	69	78	90	102	114
5000	12½	19	25	31	37½	50	62½	75	87½	100	112	125

INDEX

Appendix

Extract from

Treatise on Hydraulics

by Mansfield Merriman, 1902.

(Articles 146 to 164)

WATER WHEELS.

ARTICLE 146. CONDITIONS OF HIGH EFFICIENCY.

A hydraulic motor is an apparatus for utilizing the energy of a waterfall. It generally consists of a wheel which is caused to revolve, either by the weight of water falling from a higher to a lower level, or by the dynamic pressure due to the change in direction and velocity of a moving stream. When the water enters at only one part of the circumference the apparatus is called a water wheel; when it enters around the entire circumference it is called a turbine. In this chapter and the next these two classes of motors will be discussed in order to determine the conditions which render them most efficient.

The efficiency e of a motor ought, if possible, to be independent of the amount of water used, or if not, it should be the greatest when the water supply is low. This is very difficult to attain. It should be noted, however, that it is not the mere variation in the quantity of water which causes the efficiency to vary, but it is the losses of head which are consequent thereon. For instance, when water is low, gates must be lowered to diminish the area of orifices, and this produces sudden changes of section which diminish the effective head h. A complete theoretic expression for the efficiency will hence not include W, the weight of water supplied per second, but it should, if possible, include the losses of energy or head which result when W varies. The actual efficiency of a motor can only be determined by tests with a friction brake; the theoretic efficiency, as deduced from formulas like those of Chapter XI, will as a rule be higher than the actual, because it is impossible to formulate accurately all the sources of loss. Nevertheless, the deduction and discussion of formulas for theoretic efficiency is very important for the correct understanding and successful construction of hydraulic motors.

The theoretic energy per second of W pounds of water falling through a height of h feet, or moving with a velocity v, is

$$K = Wh = W\frac{v^2}{2g}.$$

The actual work per second equals the theoretic energy minus all the losses of energy. These losses may be divided into two classes: first, those caused by the transformation of energy into heat; and second, those due to the velocity v_1 with which the water reaches the level of the tail race. The first class includes losses in friction, losses in foam and eddies consequent upon sudden changes in cross-section, or from allowing the entering water to dash improperly against surfaces; let the loss of work due to this be Wh', in which h' is the head lost by these causes. The second loss is due merely to the fact that the departing water carries away the energy $W\frac{v_1^2}{2g}$. The work per second imparted to the wheel then is

$$k = W\left(h - h' - \frac{v_1^2}{2g}\right);$$

and dividing this by the theoretic energy, the efficiency is

$$e = 1 - \frac{h'}{h} - \left(\frac{v_1}{v}\right)^2. \quad . \quad . \quad . \quad . \quad . \quad . \quad (90)$$

This formula, although very general, must be the basis of all discussions on the theory of water-wheels and motors. It shows that e can only become unity when $h' = 0$ and $v_1 = 0$, whence the two following fundamental requirements must be fulfilled in order to secure high efficiency:

1. The water must enter and pass through the wheel without losing energy in friction and foam.
2. The water must reach the level of the tail race without absolute velocity.

These two requirements are expressed in popular language by the maxim, well known among engineers, "the water must enter the wheel without shock and leave without velocity." Here the word shock means that method of introducing the water which produces foam and eddies.

The friction of the wheel upon its bearings is included in the lost work when the power and efficiency are actually measured as described in Art. 124. But as this is not a hydraulic loss, it should not be included in the lost work k' when discussing the wheel merely as a user of water, as will be done in this chapter. The amount lost in shaft and journal friction in good constructions may be estimated at 2 or 3 per cent of the theoretic energy, so that in discussing the hydraulic losses the maximum value of e will not be unity, but about 0.98 or 0.97. This may perhaps be rendered slightly smaller by the friction of the wheel upon the air or water in which it moves, and which will here not be regarded.

ARTICLE 147. OVERSHOT WHEELS.

In the overshot wheel the water acts largely by its weight. Fig. 100 shows an end view or vertical section, which so fully illustrates its action that no detailed explanation is necessary. The total fall from the surface of the water in the head race or flume to the surface in the tail race is called h. The weight of water delivered per second is represented by W; then the theoretic energy of the fall per second is Wh. It is required to determine the conditions which will render the work of the wheel as near to Wh as possible.

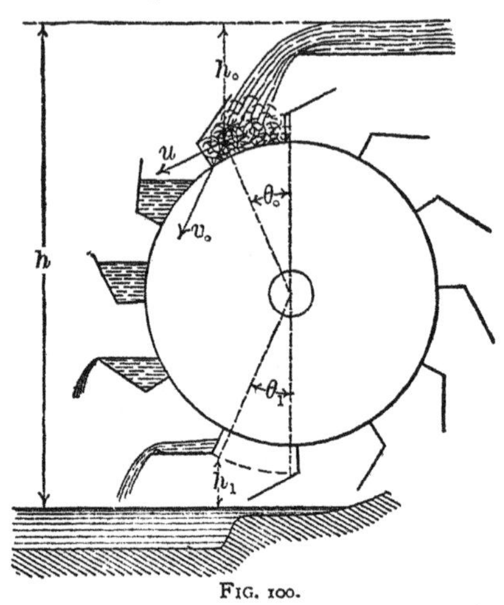

FIG. 100.

The total fall may be divided into three parts—that in which the water is filling the buckets, that in which the water is descending in the filled buckets, and that which remains after the buckets are emptied. Let the first of these parts be called h_0, and the last h_1. In falling the distance h_0 the water acquires a velocity v_0 which is approximately equal to $\sqrt{2gh_0}$, and then striking the buckets this is reduced to u, the tangential velocity of the wheel, whereby a loss of energy in impact occurs. It then descends through the distance $h - h_0 - h_1$ acting by its weight alone, and finally dropping out of the buckets, reaches the level of the tail race with a velocity which causes a second loss of energy. Let h' be the head lost in entering the buckets, and let v_1 be the velocity of the water as it reaches the tail race. Then the efficiency of the wheel is given by the general formula (90), or

$$e = 1 - \frac{h'}{h} - \frac{v_1^2}{v^2};$$

and to apply it, the values of h' and v_1 are to be found. In this equation v is the velocity due to the head h, or $v = \sqrt{2gh}$.

The head lost when a stream of water with the velocity v_0 is enlarged in section so as to have the smaller velocity u, is, as proved in Art. 68,

$$h' = \frac{(v_0 - u)^2}{2g} = \frac{v_0^2 - 2v_0u + u^2}{2g}.$$

The velocity v_1 with which the water reaches the tail race depends upon the velocity u and the height h_1. Its energy as it leaves the buckets is $W\frac{u^2}{2g}$, and that acquired in the fall h_1 is Wh_1; the sum of these must be equal to the resultant energy, $W\frac{v_1^2}{2g}$, whence the value of v_1 is

$$v_1 = \sqrt{u^2 + 2gh_1}.$$

Inserting these values of h' and v_1 in the formula for e, and placing for v^2 its equivalent $2gh$, there is found

$$e = 1 - \frac{v_0^2 - 2v_0u + 2u^2 + 2gh_1}{2gh}.$$

The value of u which renders e a maximum is by the usual method found to be

$$u = \tfrac{1}{2}v_0;$$

or the velocity of the wheel should be one-half that of the entering water. Inserting this value, the efficiency corresponding to the advantageous velocity is

$$e = 1 - \frac{\frac{1}{2}v_0^2 + 2gh_1}{2gh};$$

and lastly, replacing v_0^2 by its value $2gh_0$, it becomes

$$e = 1 - \frac{1}{2}\frac{h_0}{h} - \frac{h_1}{h}; \quad . \quad . \quad . \quad . \quad . \quad . \quad . \quad (91)$$

which is the theoretic maximum efficiency of the overshot wheel.

This investigation shows that one-half of the entrance fall h_0 and the whole of the exit fall h_1 are lost, and it is hence plain that in order to make e as large as possible both h_0 and h_1 should be as small as possible. The fall h_0 is made small by making the radius of the wheel large; but it cannot be zero, for then no water would enter the wheel: it is generally taken so as to make the angle θ_0 about 10 or 15 degrees. The fall h_1 is made small by giving to the buckets a form which will retain the water as long as possible. As the water really leaves the wheel at several points along the lower circumference, the value of h_1 cannot usually be determined with exactness.

The practical advantageous velocity of the overshot wheel, as determined by the method of Art. 134, is found to be about $0.4v_0$, and its efficiency is found to be high, ranging from 70 to 90 per cent. In times of drought, when the water supply is low, and it is desirable to utilize all the power available, its efficiency is the highest, since then the buckets are but partly filled and h_1 becomes small. Herein lies the great advantage of the overshot wheel; its disadvantage is in its large size and the expense of construction and maintenance.

The number of buckets and their depth are governed by no laws except those of experience. Usually the number of buckets is about $5r$ or $6r$, if r is the radius of the wheel in feet, and their radial depth is from 10 to 15 inches. The breadth of the wheel parallel to its axis depends upon the quantity of water supplied, and should be so great that the buckets are not fully filled with water, in order that they may retain it as long as possible and thus make h_1 small. The wheel should be set with its outer circumference at the level of the tail water.

ARTICLE 148. BREAST WHEELS.

The breast wheel is applicable to small falls, and the action of the water is partly by impulse and partly by weight. As represented in Fig. 101, water from a reservoir is admitted through an orifice upon the wheel under the head h_0 with the velocity v_0; the water being then confined between the vanes and the curved breast acts by its weight through a distance h_2,

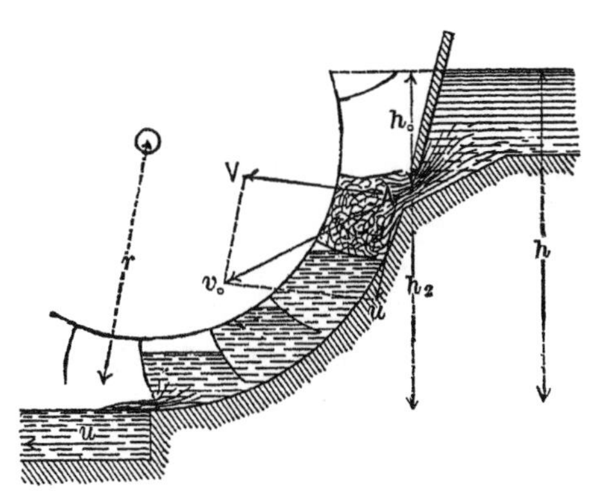

FIG. 101.

which is approximately equal to $h - h_0$, until finally it is released at the level of the tail race and departs with the velocity u, which is the same as that of the circumference of the wheel. The total energy of the water being Wh, the work of the wheel is eWh, if e be its efficiency.

The reasoning of the last article may be applied to the breast wheel, h_1 being made equal to zero, and the expression there deduced for e may be regarded as an approximate value of its theoretic efficiency. It appears, then, that e will be the greater the smaller the fall h_0; but owing to leakage between the wheel and the curved breast, which cannot be theoretically estimated, and which is less for high velocities than for low ones, it is not desirable to make v_0 and h_0 small. The efficiency of the breast wheel is hence materially less than that of the overshot, and usually ranges from 50 to 80 per cent, the lower values being for small wheels.

Another method of determining the theoretic efficiency of the breast wheel is to discuss the action of the water in entering and leaving the vanes as a case of impulse. Let at the point of entrance Av_0 and Au be drawn parallel and equal to the velocities v_0 and u, the former being that of the entering water and the latter that of the vanes. Let α be the angle between v_0 and u, which may be called the angle of approach. Then the dynamic pressure exerted by the water in entering upon and leaving the vanes is, from Art. 133,

$$P = W\frac{v_0 \cos\alpha - u}{g},$$

and the work performed by it per second is

$$k_0 = W\frac{(v_0 \cos\alpha - u)u}{g}.$$

This has its maximum value when

$$u = \tfrac{1}{2}v_0 \cos\alpha,$$

and the corresponding work of the impulse is

$$k_0 = W\frac{v_0^2 \cos^2\alpha}{4g}.$$

Adding this to the work Wh_2 done by the weight of the water, the total work of the wheel when running at the advantageous velocity is found to be

$$k = W\left(\frac{v_0^2 \cos^2\alpha}{4g} + h_2\right);$$

or if v_0^2 be replaced by its value $c_1^2 . 2gh_0$, where c_1 is the coefficient of velocity as determined by the rules of Chapters IV and VI,

$$k = W(\tfrac{1}{2}c_1^2 \cos^2 \alpha . h_0 + h_2),$$

whence the theoretic efficiency is

$$e = \tfrac{1}{2}c_1^2 \cos^2 \alpha \frac{h_0}{h} + \frac{h_2}{h}. \quad . \quad . \quad . \quad . \quad . \quad . \quad . \quad (92)$$

If in this expression h_2 be replaced by $h - h_0$, and if $c_1 = 1$ and $\alpha = 0°$, this reduces to the same value as found for the overshot wheel. The angle α, however, cannot be zero, for then the direction of the entering water would be tangential to the wheel, and it could not impinge upon the vanes; its value, however, should be small, say from 10° to 25°. The coefficient c_1 is to be rendered large by making the orifice of discharge with well-rounded inner corners so as to avoid contraction and the losses incident thereto. The above formulas cannot be relied upon in practice to give close values of k and e, on account of losses by foam and leakage along the curved breast, which of course cannot be algebraically expressed.

ARTICLE 149. UNDERSHOT WHEELS.

The common undershot wheel has plane radial vanes, and the water passes beneath it in a direction nearly horizontal. It may then be regarded as a breast wheel where the action is entirely by impulse, so that in the preceding equations h_2 becomes 0, h_0 becomes h, and α will be 0°. The theoretic efficiency then is

$$e = \tfrac{1}{2}c_1^2. \quad . \quad . \quad . \quad . \quad . \quad . \quad . \quad . \quad (92)'$$

In the best constructions c_1 is nearly unity, so that it may be concluded that the maximum efficiency of the undershot wheel is about 0.5. Experiment shows that its actual efficiency varies from 0.20 to 0.40, and that the advantageous velocity is about $0.4v_0$ instead of $0.5v_0$. The lowest efficiencies are obtained from wheels placed in an unlimited flowing current, as upon a scow anchored in a stream; and the highest from those where the stream beneath the wheel is confined by walls so as to prevent the water from spreading laterally.

The Poncelet wheel, so called from its distinguished inventor, has curved vanes, which are so arranged that the water leaves them tangentially, with its absolute velocity less than that of the velocity of the wheel. If in Fig. 101 the fall h_2 be very small, and the vanes be curved more than represented, it will exhibit the main features of the Poncelet wheel. The water entering with the absolute velocity v_0 takes the velocity u of the vane and the velocity V relative to the vane. Passing then under the wheel, its dynamic pressure performs work; and on leaving the vane its relative velocity V is probably nearly the same as that at entrance. Then if V be drawn tangent to the vane at the point of exit, and u tangent to the circumference, their resultant will be v_1, the absolute velocity of exit, which will be much less than u. Consequently the energy carried away by the departing water is less than in the usual forms of breast and undershot wheels, and it is found by experiment that the efficiency may be as high as 60 per cent.

In Fig. 102 is shown a portion of a Poncelet wheel. At A the water enters the wheel through a nozzle-like opening with the absolute velocity v_0 and at B it leaves with the absolute velocity v_1. In the figure A and B have the same elevation. At A the entering stream makes the approach angle α with the circumference of the wheel and the same angle with the vane, so that the relative velocity V is equal to the velocity of the outer circumference u. If h be the head on A the theoretic work of the water is Wh, and the work of the wheel is

$$k = W\frac{v_0^2 - v_1^2}{2g},$$

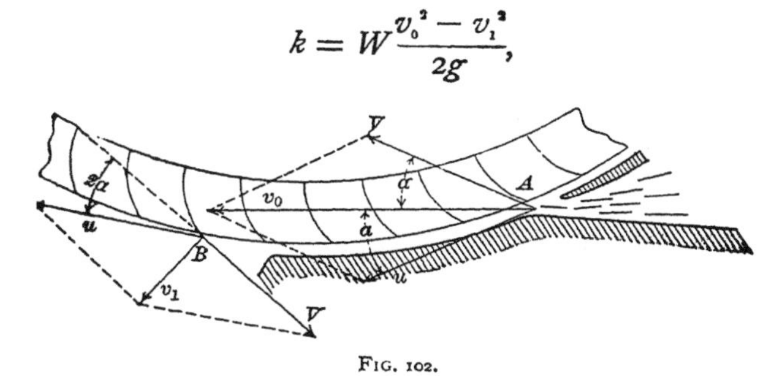

FIG. 102.

and the efficiency, neglecting friction and leakage, is

$$e = \frac{v_0^2 - v_1^2}{2gh}.$$

Now, let c_1 be the coefficient of velocity of the entrance orifice, then $v_0 = c_1\sqrt{2gh}$. From the parallelograms at A and B,

$$u = \frac{v_0}{2\cos\alpha}, \qquad v_1 = 2u\sin\alpha = v_0\tan\alpha,$$

and hence the efficiency reduces to

$$e = c_1^2(1 - \tan^2\alpha). \quad . \quad . \quad . \quad . \quad . \quad . \quad (93)$$

If $c_1 = 1$ and $\alpha = 0$, the efficiency becomes unity. In the best constructions c_1 may be made from 0.95 to 0.98, but α cannot be a very small angle, since then no water could enter the wheel. If $\alpha = 30°$ and $c_1 = 0.95$ the efficiency is 0.60, which is probably a higher value than usually attained in practice. If the velocity u be greater or less than $\frac{1}{2}v_0/\cos\alpha$, the efficiency will be lowered on account of shock and foam at A (Art. 133).

ARTICLE 150. VERTICAL IMPULSE WHEELS.

A vertical wheel like Fig. 102, but having smaller vanes against which the water is delivered from a nozzle, is often called an impulse wheel, or a "hurdy-gurdy" wheel. The Pelton wheel, the Cascade wheel, and other forms, can be purchased in several sizes, and are convenient on account of their portability. Fig. 103 shows an outline sketch of such a wheel with the vanes somewhat exaggerated in size. The simplest vanes are radial planes as at *A*, but these give a low efficiency. Curved vanes, as at *B*, are generally used, as these cause the water to turn backward, opposite to the direction of the motion, and thus to leave the wheel with a low absolute velocity (Art. 134). In the plan of the wheel it is seen that the vanes may be arranged so as also to turn the water sidewise while deflecting it backward. The experiments of BROWNE* show that with plane radial vanes the highest efficiency was 40.2 per cent, while with curved vanes or cups 82.5 per cent was attained. The velocity of the vanes which gave the highest efficiency was in each case almost exactly one-half the velocity of the jet.

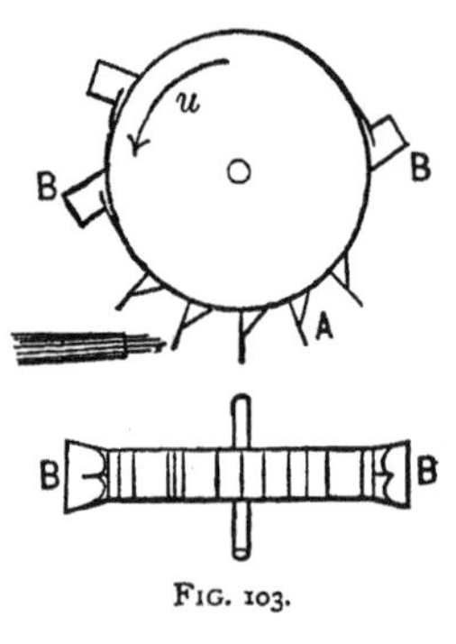

FIG. 103.

The Pelton wheel is used under high heads, and also being of small size it has a high velocity. The effective head is that measured at the entrance of the nozzle by a pressure gauge, corrected for velocity of approach and the loss in the nozzle by formula (39)'. These wheels are wholly of iron, and are provided with a casing to prevent the spattering of the water. Fig. 104 shows a form with three nozzles, by which three streams are applied at different parts of the circumference, in

* BOWIE'S Practical Treatise on Hydraulic Mining, p. 193.

order to obtain a greater power than by a single nozzle, or, by using smaller nozzles, in order to obtain a greater speed. For an effective head of 100 feet the following quantities are given

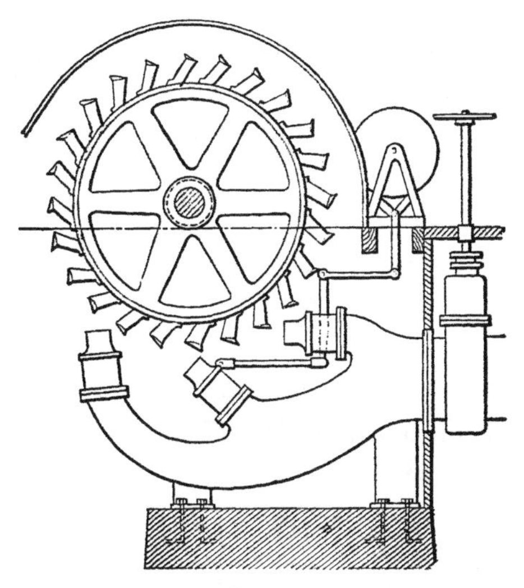

FIG. 104.

by the manufacturers for different sizes of Pelton wheels having only a single nozzle:

Diameter in feet,	1,	2,	3,	4,	6
Cubic feet per minute,	8.29,	44.19,	99.52,	176.75,	398.08
Revolutions per minute,	726,	363,	242,	181,	121
Horse-powers,	1.40,	7.49,	16.84,	29.93,	67.36

which imply an efficiency of 85 per cent.

The general theory of these vertical impulse wheels is the same as that given for moving vanes in Art. 134. Owing to the high velocity, more or less shock occurs at entrance, and as the angle of exit β cannot be made small, the water leaves the vanes with more or less absolute velocity. The losses in the conduit pipe cannot be fairly charged against the wheel, but these can be made as small as possible by using a nozzle of such diameter as will furnish a stream of maximum horse-power. Equation (64) of Art. 85 is a general expression for the velocity in the pipe, h being the total head on the nozzle, l the length and d the diameter of the pipe, and d_1 the diameter of the nozzle. Let all the resistances except that due to friction in the pipe be neglected; then the velocity of flow from the nozzle is expressed by the formula,

$$v_1 = \frac{d^2}{d_1^2}\sqrt{\frac{2gh}{f\frac{l}{d} + \frac{d^4}{d_1^4}}},$$

in which f is the friction factor whose mean value is about 0.02. Let w be the weight of a cubic foot of water: then the theoretic work of the jet per second is

$$K = w \,.\, \tfrac{1}{4}\pi d_1^2 \,.\, v_1 \,.\, \frac{v_1^2}{2g} = \frac{\pi w}{8g}\left(\frac{2ghd^5 d_1^{\frac{4}{3}}}{fld_1^4 + d^5}\right)^{\frac{3}{2}},$$

and the value of d_1 which renders this a maximum is, by help of the usual method of differentiation, found to be

$$d_1 = \sqrt[4]{\frac{d^5}{2fl}}.$$

As an example let a pipe be 1200 feet long and one foot in diameter: then, taking for f the mean value 0.2, there is found $d_1 = 0.38$ feet and hence a $4\frac{1}{2}$-inch nozzle is required to give the maximum power. This result may be revised, if thought necessary, by finding the velocity in the pipe, and thus getting a better value of f from Table XVI. If the head be 100 feet, this velocity is found to be 9.3 feet per second, whence $f =$ 0.018, and on repeating the computation there is found $d_1 =$ 0.39 feet $=$ 4.68 inches.

ARTICLE 151. HORIZONTAL IMPULSE WHEELS.

When a wheel is placed with its plane horizontal and is driven by a stream of water from a nozzle, as in Fig. 105, it is called a horizontal impulse wheel. There are two forms called the outward-flow and the inward-flow wheel. In the former the water enters the wheel upon the inner and leaves it upon the

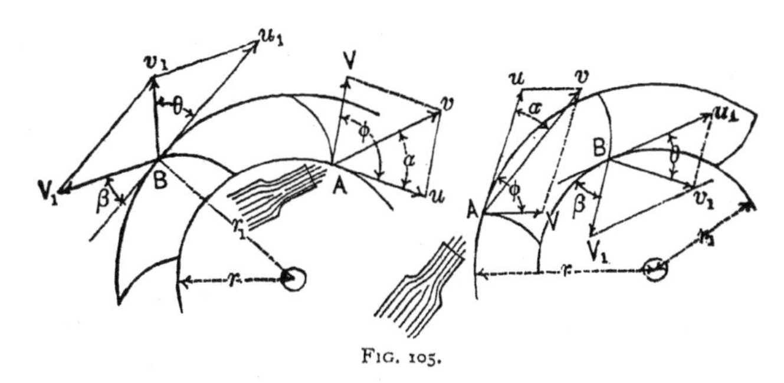

FIG. 105.

outer circumference, and in the other the reverse is the case. The water issuing from the nozzle with the velocity v impinges upon the vanes, and in passing through the wheel alters both its direction and its absolute velocity, thus transforming its energy into useful work. The energy of the entering water is $W\frac{v^2}{2g}$, and that of the departing water is $W\frac{v_1^2}{2g}$, if v_1 be its absolute velocity. The work imparted to the wheel then is

$$k = W\left(\frac{v^2}{2g} - \frac{v_1^2}{2g}\right),$$

and dividing this by the theoretic energy, the efficiency is

$$e = 1 - \frac{v_1^2}{v^2}.$$

This is the same as the general formula (90) if $h' = 0$, that is, if losses in foam and friction are disregarded, and if the wheel is set at the level of the tail race. It is now required to state the conditions which will render these losses and also the velocity v_1 as small as possible. The reasoning will be general and applicable to both outward- and inward-flow wheels.

At the point A where the water enters the wheel let the parallelogram of velocities be drawn, the absolute velocity of entrance being resolved into its two components, the velocity u of the wheel at that point, and the velocity V relative to the vane; let the approach angle between u and v be called α, and the entrance angle between u and V be called ϕ. At the point B where the water leaves the wheel let V_1 be its velocity relative to the vane, and u_1 the velocity of the wheel at that point; then their resultant is v_1, the absolute velocity of exit. Let the exit angle between V_1 and the reverse direction of u_1 be called β. The directions of the velocities u and u_1 are of course tangential to the circumferences at the points A and B. Let r and r_1 be the radii of these circumferences; then the velocities of revolution are directly as the radii, or $ur_1 = u_1r$.

In order that the water may enter the wheel without shock and foam, the relative velocity V should be tangent to the vane at A, so that the water may smoothly glide along them. This will be the case if the wheel is run at such speed that the parallelogram at A can be formed, or whenthe velocities u and v are proportional to the sines of the angles opposite them in the triangle Auv. The velocity v_1 will be rendered very small by running the impulse wheel at such speed that the velocities

u_1 and V_1 are equal, since then the parallelogram at B becomes a rhombus, and the diagonal v_1 is very small. Hence

$$\frac{u}{v} = \frac{\sin(\phi - \alpha)}{\sin \phi} \quad \text{and} \quad u_1 = V_1 \quad . \quad . \quad . \quad (94)$$

are the two conditions of maximum efficiency.

Now, referring to the formula (88) of Art. 136, which expresses the effect of centrifugal force on the water in revolving vanes, it is seen that if $u_1 = V_1$, then also $u = V$. But u cannot equal V unless $\phi = 2\alpha$, and then $u = v/2 \cos \alpha$, which is the advantageous velocity of the circumference at A. Therefore the two conditions above reduce to

$$\phi = 2\alpha \quad \text{and} \quad u = \frac{v}{2 \cos \alpha}, \quad . \quad . \quad . \quad (95)$$

which show how the wheel should be built and what speed it should have to secure the greatest efficiency. When this speed obtains the absolute velocity v_1 is

$$v_1 = 2u_1 \sin \tfrac{1}{2}\beta = 2u\frac{r_1}{r} \sin \tfrac{1}{2}\beta = v\frac{r_1}{r} \frac{\sin \frac{1}{2}\beta}{\cos \alpha},$$

and the corresponding maximum efficiency is

$$e = 1 - \frac{r_1^2}{r^2} \frac{\sin^2 \frac{1}{2}\beta}{\cos^2 \alpha}. \quad . \quad . \quad . \quad . \quad . \quad (96)$$

by the discussion of which proper values of the angles β and α can be derived.

This formula shows that both the approach angle α and the exit angle β should be small in order to give high efficiency, but they cannot be zero, as then no water could pass through the wheel; values of from 15 to 30 degrees are usual in practice. It also shows that β is more important than α, and if β be small α may sometimes be made 40 or 45 degrees.

The condition $V_1 = u_1$ renders the absolute exit velocity v_1 very small, but it does not give its true minimum. This will be obtained by making $V_1 = u_1 \cos \beta$, so that the direction of v_1 is normal to that of V_1, and thus $v_1 = u_1 \sin \beta$. The discussion of water-wheels and turbines under this condition of the true minimum leads to very complex formulas, and hence in this work, as in many others, the simpler condition $V_1 = u_1$ is adopted. It will be an excellent exercise for the student to deduce (96) for the condition $V_1 = u_1 \cos \beta$.

Article 152. Downward-flow Wheels.

In the impulse wheels thus far considered the water leaves the vanes in a horizontal direction. Another form used less frequently is that of a horizontal wheel driven by water issuing from an inclined nozzle so that it passes downward along the vanes without approaching or receding from the axis. Fig. 106 shows an outline plan of such an impulse wheel and a development of a part of a cylindrical section. Let v be the velocity of the entering stream, u that of the wheel at the point where it strikes the vanes, and v_1 the absolute velocity of the departing water. At the entrance A the direction of v makes with that of u the approach angle α, and the direction of the relative velocity V makes with that of u the entrance angle ϕ. The water then passes over the vane, and, neglecting friction, issues at B with the same relative velocity V, whose direction makes the exit angle β with the plane of motion.

The condition that impact and foam shall be avoided at A

is fulfilled by making V tangent to the vane, and the condition that the absolute velocity of exit v_1 shall be small is fulfilled by

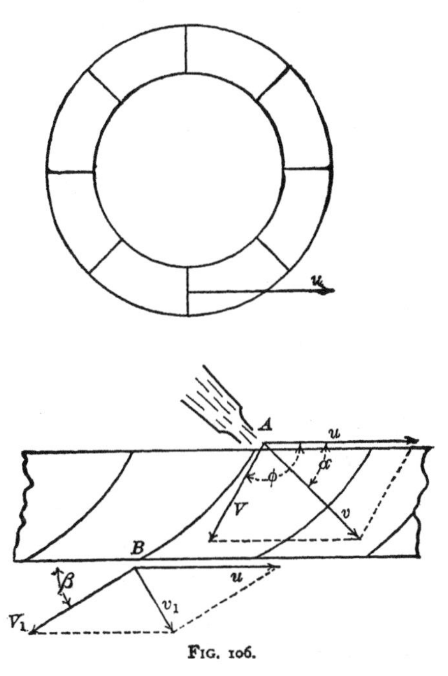

FIG. 106.

making the velocities u and V equal at B. Hence, as in the last article, the best construction is to make $\phi = 2\alpha$, and the best speed of the wheel is $u = v/2 \cos \alpha$. Also by the same reasoning the efficiency under these conditions is

$$e = 1 - \frac{\sin^2 \frac{1}{2}\beta}{\cos^2 \alpha},$$

which shows that α, and especially β, should be a small angle to give a high numerical value of e. For instance, if both these angles are 30 degrees, the efficiency is 0.921, but if $\alpha =$ 45° and $\beta = 10°$, the efficiency is 0.940.

Although these wheels are but little used, there seems to be no hydraulic reason why they should not be employed with a success equal to or greater than that attained by vertical impulse wheels. It will be possible to arrange several nozzles around the circumference, and thus to secure a high power with a small wheel. The fall of the water through the vertical distance between *A* and *B* will also add slightly to the power and perhaps also to the resulting efficiency.

ARTICLE 153. SPECIAL FORMS.

Numerous varieties of the water wheels above described have been used, but the variation lies in mechanical details rather than in the introduction of any new hydraulic principles. In order that a wheel may be a success it must furnish power as cheaply or cheaper than steam or other motors, and to this end compactness, durability, and low cost of installation and maintenance are essential.

A variety of the overshot wheel, called the back-pitch wheel, has been built in which the water is introduced on the back instead of on the front of the wheel. The buckets are hence differently arranged from those of the usual form, and the wheel revolves also in an opposite direction.

One of the largest overshot wheels ever constructed is at Laxey, on the west coast of England. It is 72½ feet in diameter, about 10 feet in width, and is supposed to furnish about 150 horse-power, which is used for pumping water out of a mine.

A breast wheel with very long curved vanes extending over nearly a fourth of the circumference has been used for small falls, the water entering directly from the penstock without impulse, so that the action is that of weight alone. These are made of iron and give a high efficiency.

Undershot wheels with curved floats for use in the open current of a river have been employed, but in order to obtain much power they require to be large in size, and hence have not been able to compete with other forms. The great amount of power wasted in all rivers should, however, incite inventors to devise wheels that can economically utilize it.

The conical wheel, or Danaïde, is an ancient form of downward-flow impulse wheel, in which the water approaches the axis as it descends, and thus its relative motion is decreased by the centrifugal force. The theory of this is almost precisely the same as that of an inward-flow impulse wheel, and there seems to be no hydraulic reason why it should not give a high efficiency. Another form of Danaïde has two or more vertical vanes attached to an axis, which are enclosed in a conical case to prevent the lateral escape of the water.

CHAPTER XIV.

TURBINES.

ARTICLE 154. THE REACTION WHEEL.

The reaction wheel, sometimes called Barker's mill, consists of a number of hollow arms connected with a hollow vertical shaft, as shown in Fig. 107. The water issues from the ends of the arms in a direction opposite to that of their motion, and by the dynamic pressure due to its reaction the energy of the water is transformed into useful work. Let the head of water CC in the shaft be h; then the pressure-head BB which causes the flow from the arms is greater than h, on account of centrifugal force. Let u_1 be the absolute velocity of the exit orifices and V_1 be the velocity of discharge relative to the wheel; then, as shown in Art. 29, and also in Art. 137,

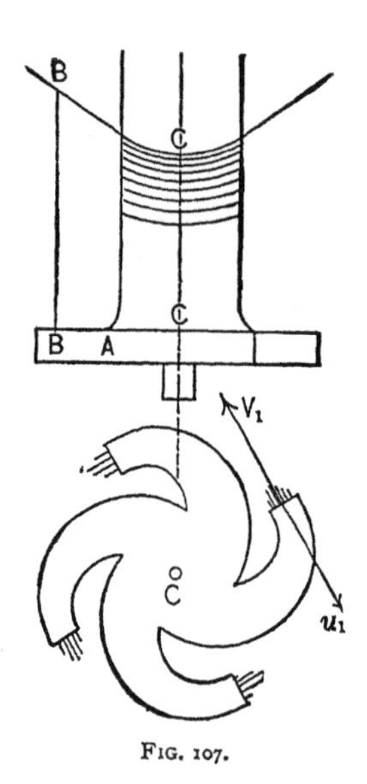

FIG. 107.

$$V_1 = \sqrt{2gh + u_1^2}.$$

The absolute velocity v_1 of the issuing water now is

$$v_1 = V_1 - u_1 = \sqrt{2gh + u_1^2} - u_1.$$

It is seen at once that the efficiency can never reach unity unless $v_1 = 0$, which requires that $V_1 = u_1$. This, however, can only occur when $u_1 = \infty$, since the above formula shows that V_1 must be greater than u_1 for any finite values of h and u_1. To deduce an expression for the efficiency the work of the wheel $W\left(h - \frac{v_1^2}{2g}\right)$ is to be divided by the total theoretic work Wh, and

$$e = 1 - \frac{v_1^2}{2gh} = 1 - \frac{(V_1 - u_1)^2}{V_1^2 - u_1^2} = \frac{2u_1}{V_1 + u_1}, \quad . \quad . \quad (97)$$

which shows, as before, that e equals unity when $V_1 = u_1 = \infty$. If $V_1 = 2u_1$, the value of e is 0.667; if $V_1 = 3u_1$, the value of e is reduced to 0.50.

This investigation indicates that the efficiency of a reaction wheel increases with its speed. If a_1 be the area of the exit orifices and w the weight of a cubic unit of water, the weight of the water discharged in one second is wa_1V_1, which becomes infinite when $V_1 = u_1 = \infty$. Nothing approaching this can be realized, and on account of losses due to friction a very high speed is impracticable. The reaction wheel, indeed, is like the jet propeller (Art. 141).

To consider the effect of friction in the arms, let c_1 be the coefficient of velocity (Chapter VI), so that

$$V_1 = c_1 \sqrt{2gh + u_1^2}.$$

Then the effective work of the wheel is

$$k = W\frac{(c_1 \sqrt{2gh + u_1^2} - u_1)u_1}{g},$$

and the efficiency is

$$e = \frac{c_1 u_1 \sqrt{2gh + u_1^2} - u_1^2}{gh}.$$

The value of u_1, which renders this a maximum, is

$$u_1^2 = \frac{gh}{\sqrt{1 - c_1^2}} - gh,$$

and this reduces the value of the efficiency to

$$e = 1 - \sqrt{1 - c_1^2}. \quad . \quad . \quad . \quad . \quad . \quad . \quad . \quad . \quad . \quad (98)$$

If $c_1 = 1$, there is no loss in friction, and $u_1 = \infty$ and $e = 1$, as before deduced. If $c_1 = 0.94$, the advantageous velocity u_1 is very nearly $\sqrt{2gh}$, and e is 0.66; hence the influence of friction in diminishing the efficiency is very great. In order to make c_1 large, the end of the arm where the water enters must be well rounded to prevent contraction, and the interior surface must be smooth. If the inner end has sharp square edges, as in a standard tube (Art. 61), c_1 is 0.82, and e becomes 0.43.

The reaction wheel is not now used as a hydraulic motor on account of its low efficiency. Even when run at high speeds the efficiency is low on account of the greater friction and resistance of the air. By experiments on a wheel one meter in diameter under a head of 1.3 feet WEISBACH found a maximum efficiency of 67 per cent when the velocity of revolution u_1 was $\sqrt{2gh}$. When u_1 was $2\sqrt{2gh}$ the efficiency was nothing, or all the energy was consumed in frictional resistances.

The reaction wheel is here introduced at the beginning of the discussion of turbines mainly to call attention to the fact that the discharge varies with the speed. Although sometimes called a turbine, it can scarcely be properly considered as belonging to that class of motors.

Article 155. Classification of Turbines.

A turbine wheel has been defined as one in which the water enters around the entire circumference instead of upon one portion, so that all the moving vanes are simultaneously acted upon by the dynamic pressure of the water as it changes its direction and velocity. Turbines are usually horizontal wheels, and like the impulse wheels of the last chapter they may be outward-flow, inward-flow, or downward-flow, with respect to the manner in which the water passes through them. In the outward-flow type the water enters the wheel around the entire inner circumference and passes out around the entire outer circumference (Fig. 109). In the inward-flow type the motion is the reverse (Fig. 110). In the downward-flow type the water enters around the entire upper annular openings, passes downward between the moving vanes, and leaves through the lower annulus (Fig. 115). In all cases the water in leaving the wheel should have a low absolute velocity, so that most of its energy may be surrendered to the turbine in the form of useful work.

The supply of water to a turbine is regulated by a gate or gates, which can partially or entirely close the orifices where the water enters or leaves. The guides and wheel, with the gates and the surrounding casings, are made of iron. Numerous forms with different kinds of gates and different proportions of guides and vanes are in the market. They are made of all sizes from 6 to 60 inches in diameter, and larger sizes are built for special cases. The great turbines at Niagara are of the outward-flow type, the inner diameter of a wheel being 63 inches, and each twin turbine furnishing about 5000 horse-powers. On account of their cheapness, durability, compactness, and high efficiency turbines are now more extensively used than all other kinds of hydraulic motors.

The three typical classes of turbines above described are

often called by the names of those who first invented or perfected them; thus the outward-flow is called the Fourneyron, the inward-flow the Francis, and the downward-flow the Jonval, turbine. There are also many turbines in the market in which the flow is a combination of inward and downward motion, the water entering horizontally and inward, and leaving vertically, the vanes being warped surfaces. The usual efficiency of turbines at full gate is from 70 to 85 per cent, although 90 per cent has in some cases been derived. When the gate is partly closed the efficiency in general decreases, and when the gate opening is small it becomes very low, as the test in Art. 126 shows. This is due to the loss of head consequent upon the sudden change of cross-section; and therein lies the disadvantage of the turbine, for when the water supply is low, it is important that the wheel should utilize all the power available.

Another classification is into impulse and reaction turbines. In an impulse turbine the water enters the wheel with a velocity due to the head at the point of entrance, just as it does from the nozzle which drives an impulse wheel (Art. 151). In a reaction turbine, however, the velocity of the entering water may be greater or less than that due to the head on the orifices of entrance, and, as in the reaction wheel, it is also influenced by the speed. This is due to the fact that in a reaction turbine the static pressure of the water is partially transmitted into the moving wheel, provided that the spaces between the vanes are fully filled. Any turbine may be made to act either as an impulse or a reaction turbine. If it be arranged so that the water passes through the vanes without filling them, it is an impulse turbine; if it be placed under water, or if by other means the flowing water is compelled to completely fill all the passages, it acts as a reaction turbine. As will be seen later the theory of the reaction turbine is quite different from that of the impulse turbine.

ARTICLE 156. REACTION TURBINES.

A reaction turbine is driven by the dynamic pressure of flowing water which at the same time may be under a certain degree of static pressure. If in the reaction wheel of Fig. 107 the arms be separated from the penstock at A, and be so arranged that BA revolves around the axis while AC is stationary, the resulting apparatus may be called a reaction turbine. The static pressure of the head CC can still be transmitted through the arms, so that, as in the reaction wheel, the discharge will be influenced by the speed of rotation. The general arrangement of the moving part is, however, like that of

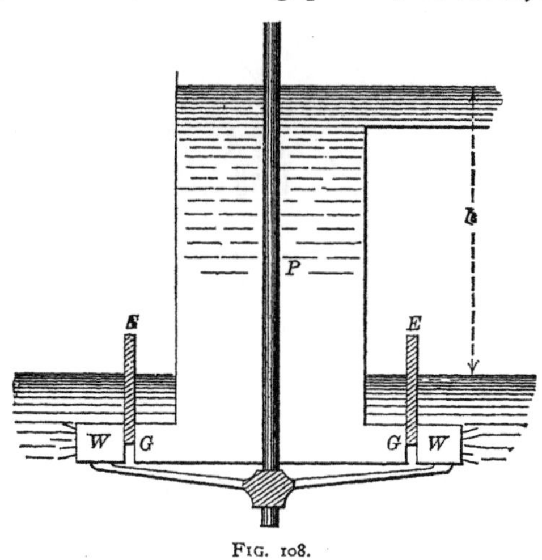

FIG. 108.

an impulse wheel, the vanes being set between two annular frames, which are attached by arms to a central axis. In Fig. 108 is a vertical section showing an outward-flow wheel W to which the water is brought by guides G from a fixed penstock

P. Between the guides and the wheel there is an annular space in which slides an annular vertical gate *E*; this serves to regulate the quantity of water, and when it is entirely depressed the wheel stops. Many other forms of gates are, however, used in the different styles of turbines found in the market.

In Figs. 109 and 110 are given horizontal and vertical sections of both the outward- and the inward-flow types, showing the arrangement of guides and vanes. The fixed guide passages

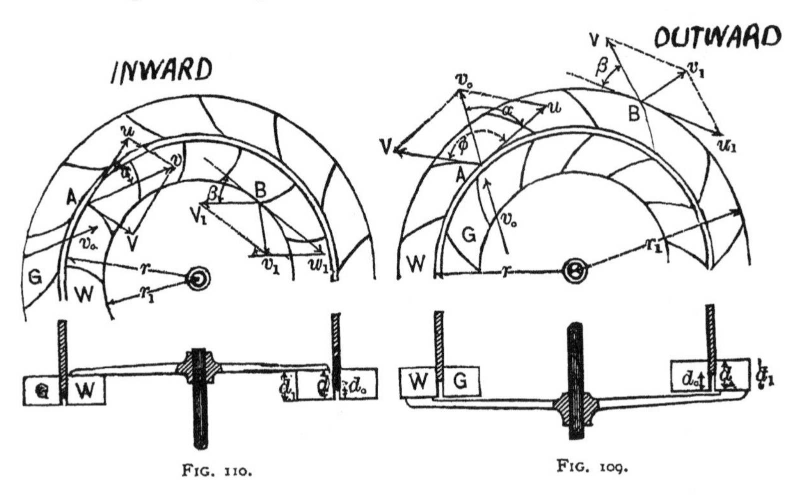

FIG. 110.

FIG. 109.

which lead the water from the penstock are marked *G*, while the moving wheel is marked *W*. It is seen that the water is introduced around the entire circumference of the wheel, and hence the quantity supplied, and likewise the power, is far greater than in the impulse wheels of the last chapter.

In order that the static pressure may be transmitted into the wheel it is placed under water, as in Fig. 108, or the exit orifices are partially closed by gates, or the air is prevented from entering them by some other device.

In Fig. 111 a Leffel turbine of the inward-flow type is illus-

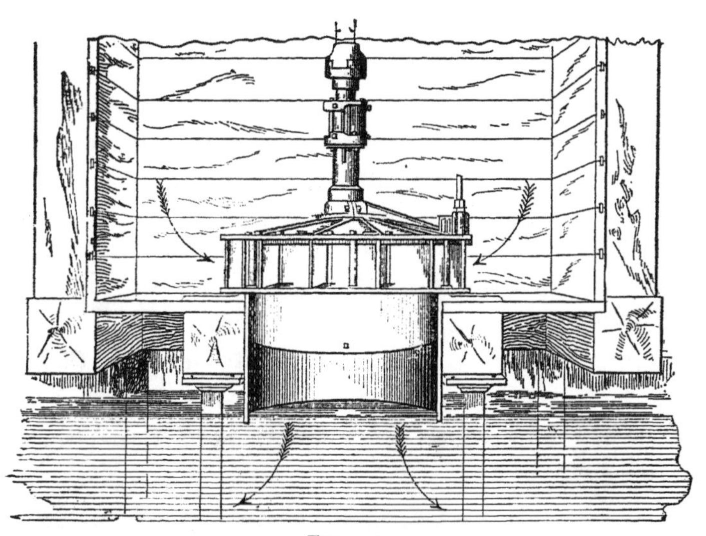

Fig. 111.

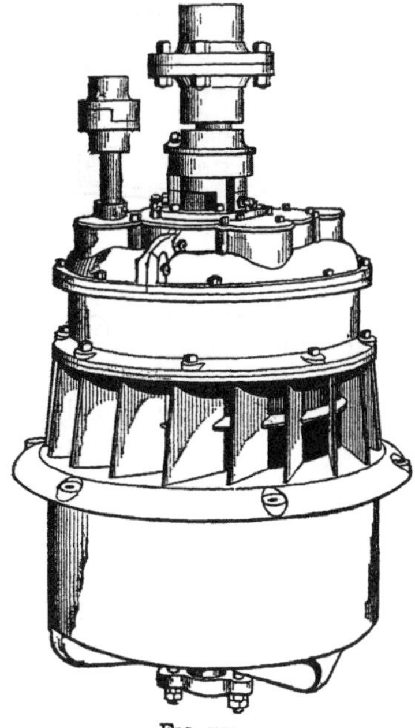

Fig. 112.

trated, the arrows showing the direction of the water as it enters and leaves. The wheel itself is not visible, it being within the enclosing case through which the water enters by the spaces between the guides. In Fig. 112 is shown a view of a Hunt turbine, which is also of the inward- and downward-flow type. In both cases the guides are seen with the small shaft for moving the gates, these being partly raised in Fig. 112. The flange at the base of the guides serves to support the weight of the entire apparatus upon the floor of the enclosing penstock, which is filled with water to the level of the head bay. The cylinder below the flange, commonly called a draught-tube, carries away the water from the wheel, and the level of the tail water should stand a little higher than its lower rim in order to prevent the introduction of air, and thus ensure that the wheel may act as a reaction turbine. Iron penstocks are frequently used instead of wooden ones, and for the pure outward- and inward-flow types the wheel is often placed below the level of the tail race.

Turbines are sometimes placed vertically on a horizontal shaft. Fig. 113 shows twin Eureka turbines thus arranged in an enclosing iron casing. The water enters through a large

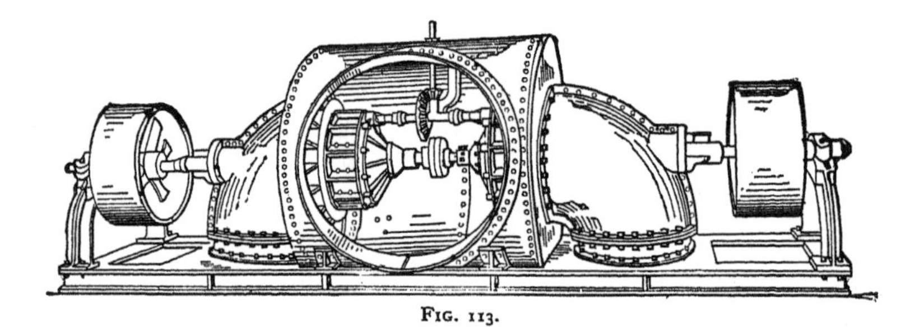

FIG. 113.

pipe attached to the circular opening, and having filled the cylindrical casing it passes through the guides, turns the wheels, and escapes by the two elbows. Large twin vertical turbines, furnishing 1200 horse-powers, have been built by the James Leffel Company.

All reaction turbines will act as impulse turbines when from any cause the passages between the vanes, or buckets, as they are generally called, are not filled with water. In this case the theory of their action is exactly like that of the impulse wheels described in the last chapter. In Arts. 157–160 reaction turbines of the simple outward- and inward-flow types will be discussed, the downward-flow type being reserved for special description and consideration in Art. 161.

ARTICLE 157. FLOW THROUGH REACTION TURBINES.

The discharge through an impulse turbine, like that for an impulse wheel, depends only on the area of the guide orifices and the effective head upon them, or $q = av = a\sqrt{2gh}$. In a reaction turbine, however, the discharge is influenced by the speed of revolution, as in the reaction wheel, and also by the areas of the entrance and exit orifices. To find an expression for this discharge let the wheel be supposed to be placed below the surface of the tail water, as in Fig. 114. Let h be the total head between the upper water level and that in the tail race, H_1 the pressure-head on the exit orifices and H the pressure-head at the gate opening as indicated by a piezometer supposed to be there inserted. Let u_1 and u be the velocities of the wheel at the exit and entrance circumference, whose radii are r_1 and r (Fig. 109). Let V_1 and V be the relative velocities of exit and entrance, and v_0 be the absolute velocity of the water as it leaves the guides and enters the wheel; v_0 may be less or greater than $\sqrt{2gh}$, depending upon the value of the pressure-head H. Let a_1, a, and a_0 be the areas of the orifices normal to the directions of V_1, V, and v_0. Now, neglecting all losses of friction between the guides, the theorem

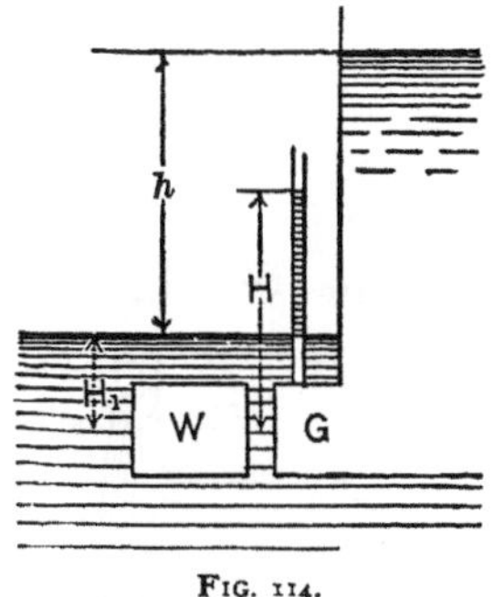

FIG. 114.

of Art. 27, that pressure-head plus velocity-head equals the total head, gives the equation

$$H + \frac{v_0^2}{2g} = h + H_1. \quad . \quad . \quad . \quad . \quad . \quad . \quad . \quad (99)$$

Also, neglecting the friction and foam in the buckets, the theorem (89) of Art. 137 gives

$$H_1 + \frac{V_1^2}{2g} - \frac{u_1^2}{2g} = H + \frac{V^2}{2g} - \frac{u^2}{2g}. \quad . \quad . \quad . \quad (100)$$

Adding these equations, the pressure-heads H_1 and H disappear, and there results the formula

$$V_1^2 - V^2 + v_0^2 = 2gh + u_1^2 - u^2. \quad . \quad . \quad . \quad (101)$$

Now, since the buckets are fully filled, the same quantity of water, q, passes in each second through each of the areas a_1, a, and a_0, and hence the three velocities have the respective values,

$$V_1 = \frac{q}{a_1}, \qquad V = \frac{q}{a}, \qquad v_0 = \frac{q}{a_0}$$

Introducing these values into the formula (101), solving for q, and multiplying by a coefficient c to account for losses in leakage and friction, the discharge per second is

$$q = c\sqrt{\frac{2gh + u_1^2 - u^2}{\frac{1}{a_1^2} - \frac{1}{a^2} + \frac{1}{a_0^2}}}. \quad . \quad . \quad . \quad . \quad (102)$$

This is the formula for the flow through a reaction turbine when the gate is fully raised. The reasoning applies to an inward flow as well as to an outward-flow wheel. In an outward-flow turbine u_1 is greater than u, and consequently the discharge increases with the speed; in an inward-flow turbine u_1 is less than u, and consequently the discharge decreases as the speed increases.

The value of the coefficient c will probably vary with the head, and also with the size of the areas a_1, a, and a_0. For the outward-flow Boyden turbine, the tests of which are given in Art. 126, it lies between 0.94 and 0.95, as the following results show, where the first four columns contain the number of the experiment, the observed head, number of revolutions per minute, and discharge in cubic feet per second. The fifth column gives the theoretic discharge computed from the above formula, taking the coefficient as unity, and the last column is

No.	h.	N.	q.	Q.	c.
21	17.16	63.5	117.01	123.1	0.950
20	17.27	70.0	118.37	125.2	0.945
19	17.33	75.0	119.53	126.8	0.943
18	17.34	80.0	121.15	128.4	0.944
17	17.21	86.0	122.41	130.0	0.942
16	17.21	93.2	124.74	132.5	0.941
15	17.19	100.0	127.73	134.9	0.947

derived by dividing the observed discharge q by the theoretic discharge Q. The discrepancy of 5 or 6 per cent is smaller than might be expected, since the formula does not consider frictional resistances.

A satisfactory formula for the discharge through a turbine when the gate is partly depressed is difficult to deduce, because the loss of head which then results can only be expressed by the help of experimental coefficients similar to those given in Art. 75 for the sliding gate in a water pipe, and the values of these for turbines are not known. It is, however, certain that for each particular gate opening the discharge is given by

$$q = m\sqrt{2gh + u_1^2 - u^2}; \quad . \quad . \quad . \quad . \quad (102)'$$

in which m depends upon the areas of the orifices and the height to which the gate is raised. For instance, in the tests of the Boyden turbine of Art. 126, the value of m is 2.815 when the proportional gate opening is 0.609, and the computed discharges will differ in no case more than one per cent from those observed; when the proportional gate opening is 0.200, the value of m is 1.357. And each turbine will have its own values of m, depending upon the area of its orifices.

It thus appears that, if the constant m be determined by experiment for different gate openings, a reaction turbine may be used as a water meter to measure the discharge with a fair degree of precision.

ARTICLE 158. THEORY OF REACTION TURBINES.

The theory of reaction turbines may be said to include two problems: first, given all the dimensions of a turbine and the head under which it works, to determine the maximum efficiency, and the corresponding speed, discharge, and power; and second, having given the head and the quantity of water, to design a turbine of high efficiency. This article deals only with the first problem, and it should be said at the outset that it cannot be fully solved theoretically, even for the best conditioned wheels, on account of losses in foam, friction, and leakage. The investigation will be limited to the case of full gate, since when the gate is partially depressed a loss of energy, due to sudden enlargement, generally results (Art. 68).

The notation will be the same as that used in Chapters XI and XIII, and as shown in Figs. 109 and 110; the reasoning will apply to both outward- and inward-flow turbines. Let r be the radius of the circumference where the water enters the wheel and r_1 that of the circumference where it leaves, let u and u_1 be the corresponding velocities of revolution; then $ur_1 = u_1 r$. Let v_0 be the absolute velocity with which the water leaves the guides and enters the wheel, and V its velocity of entrance; let α be the approach angle and ϕ be the entrance angle which these velocities make with the direction of u. At the exit circumference let V_1 be the relative velocity with which the water leaves the guides, and v_1 its absolute velocity; let β be the exit angle which V_1 makes with this circumference. Let a_0, a, and a_1 be the areas of the guide orifices, the entrance, and the exit orifices of the wheel, respectively, measured perpendicular to the directions of v_0, V, and V_1. Let d_0, d, and d_1 be the depths of these orifices; when the gate is fully raised d_0 becomes equal to d.

The areas a_0, a, a_1, neglecting the thickness of the guides and vanes, and taking the gate as fully open, have the values

$$a_0 = 2\pi r d \sin \alpha, \quad a = 2\pi r d \sin \phi, \quad a_1 = 2\pi r_1 d_1 \sin \beta;$$

and since these areas are fully filled with water,

$$q = v_0 \,.\, 2\pi r d \sin \alpha = V \,.\, 2\pi r d \sin \phi = V_1 \,.\, 2\pi r_1 d_1 \sin \beta. \quad (103)$$

These relations, together with the formulas of the last article and the geometrical conditions of the parallelograms of velocities, include the entire theory of the reaction turbine.

In order that the efficiency of the turbine may be as high as possible the water must enter tangentially to the vanes, and the absolute velocity of the issuing water must be as small as possible. The first condition will be fulfilled when u and v_0 are proportional to the sines of the angles $\phi - \alpha$ and ϕ. The second will be secured by making $u_1 = V_1$ in the parallelogram at exit, as then the diagonal v_1 becomes very small. Hence

$$\frac{u}{v_0} = \frac{\sin(\phi - \alpha)}{\sin\phi}, \quad u_1 = V_1, \quad . \quad . \quad . \quad . \quad (104)$$

are the two conditions of maximum efficiency.

Now making $V_1 = u_1$ in the third quantity of (103) and equating it to the first, there results

$$\frac{u_1}{v_0} = \frac{rd \sin\alpha}{r_1 d_1 \sin\beta} \quad \text{and} \quad \frac{u}{v_0} = \frac{r^2 d \sin\alpha}{r_1^2 d_1 \sin\beta} \quad . \quad (105)$$

Also making $V_1 = u_1$ in (101) and substituting for V^2 its value $u^2 + v_0^2 - 2uv_0 \cos\alpha$, from the triangle at A between u and v_0, there is found the important relation

$$uv_0 \cos\alpha = gh, \quad . \quad . \quad . \quad . \quad . \quad . \quad (106)$$

which gives another condition between u and v_0.

Thus three equations between two unknown quantities u and v_0 have been deduced for the case of maximum efficiency, namely,

$$\frac{u}{v_0} = \frac{\sin(\phi - \alpha)}{\sin\phi}, \quad \frac{u}{v_0} = \frac{r^2 d \sin\alpha}{r_1^2 d_1 \sin\beta}, \quad uv_0 = \frac{gh}{\cos\alpha}.$$

If the values of u and v_0 be found from the first and third equations, they are

$$u = \sqrt{\frac{gh \sin(\phi - \alpha)}{\cos\alpha \sin\phi}}, \quad v_0 = \sqrt{\frac{gh \sin\phi}{\cos\alpha \sin(\phi - \alpha)}}, \quad (107)$$

the first of which is the advantageous velocity of the circumference where the water enters, and the second is the absolute velocity with which the water leaves the guides and enters the wheel. In order, however, that these expressions may be correct, the first and second values of u/v_0 must also be equal, or

$$\frac{\sin(\phi - \alpha)}{\sin \phi} = \frac{r^2 d \sin \alpha}{r_1^2 d_1 \sin \beta}, \quad . \quad . \quad . \quad . \quad (108)$$

which is the necessary relation between the dimensions and angles of the wheel in order that this theory may apply.

For a turbine so constructed and running at the advantageous speed, the hydraulic efficiency is

$$e = 1 - \frac{v_1^2}{2gh} = 1 - \frac{2u_1^2 \sin^2 \frac{1}{2}\beta}{gh};$$

and substituting for u_1 its value in terms of u from (107) and having regard to (108), this becomes

$$e = 1 - \frac{d}{d_1} \tan \alpha \tan \tfrac{1}{2}\beta. \quad . \quad . \quad . \quad . \quad . \quad . \quad (109)$$

The discharge under the same conditions is $q = a_0 v_0$, and lastly the work of the wheel per second is $k = wqhe$.

The result of this investigation is that the general problem of investigating a given turbine cannot be solved theoretically, unless it be so built as to approximately satisfy the condition in (108). If this be the case it may be discussed by the formulas deduced. Even then no very satisfactory conclusions can be drawn from the numerical values, since the formulas do not take into account the loss by friction and that of leakage. To determine the efficiency, best speed, and power of a given turbine, the only way is to actually test it by the method described in Art. 126. The above formulas are, however, of great value in the discussion of the design of turbines.

If the coefficient of discharge of a turbine be known (Art. 157), the advantageous speed and corresponding discharge may be closely computed. For this purpose the condition $u_1 = V_1 = q/a_1$ is to be used. Inserting in this the value of q from (102) and solving for u_1, there is found

$$u_1^2 = \frac{c^2 . 2gh}{1 + c^2\frac{r^2}{r_1^2} + \frac{a_1^2}{a_0^2} - \frac{a_1^2}{a^2} - c^2}, \quad . \quad . \quad . \quad (110)$$

which gives the advantageous velocity of the circumference where the water leaves the wheel, and then by (102) the discharge can be obtained. As an example, take the case of Holyoke test No. 275, where $r_1 = 27\frac{1}{2}$ inches, $r = 21\frac{1}{2}$ inches, $h = 23.8$ feet, $a_0 = 2.066$, $a = 5.526$, $a_1 = 1.949$ square feet, $\alpha = 25\frac{1}{2}°$, $\phi = 90°$, $\beta = 11\frac{3}{4}°$. Assuming $c = 0.95$, as the turbine is similar to that investigated in the last article, the formula (110) gives $u_1 = 31.24$ feet per second, which corresponds to 130 revolutions per minute, which agrees well with the actual number, 138. The efficiency found by the test at that speed was 0.79, which is a very much less value than the above theoretic formulas will give.

ARTICLE 159. DESIGN OF REACTION TURBINES.

The design of an outward- or inward-flow turbine for a given head and discharge includes the determination of the dimensions r, r_1, d, d_1, and the angles α, β, and ϕ. These may be selected in very many different ways, and the formulas of the last article furnish a guide how to do this so as to secure a high degree of efficiency.

First, it is seen from (109) that the approach angle α and the exit angle β should be small, but that, as in other wheels, β has a greater influence than α. However, β must usually be greater for an inward-flow than for an outward-flow wheel in order to make the orifices of exit of sufficient size. For the entrance angle ϕ a good value is 90 degrees, and in this case the velocity u is always that due to one-half the head, as seen from (107). The radii r and r_1 should not differ too much, as then the frictional resistance of the flowing water and the moving wheel would be large. It is also seen that the efficiency is increased by making the exit depth d_1 greater than the entrance depth d, but usually these cannot greatly differ, and are often taken equal.

Secondly, it is seen that the dimensions and angles should be such as to satisfy the formula (108), since if this be not the case losses due to impact at entrance will occur which will render the other formulas of little value.

As a numerical illustration let it be required to design an outward-flow reaction turbine which shall use 120 cubic feet per second under a head of 18 feet and make 100 revolutions per minute. Let the entrance angle ϕ be taken at 90 degrees, then from (107) the best velocity of the inner circumference is

$$u = \sqrt{32.16 \times 18} = 24.06 \text{ feet per second,}$$

and hence the inner radius of the wheel is

$$r = \frac{60 \times 24.06}{2\pi \times 100} = 2.298 \text{ feet.}$$

Now let the outer radius of the wheel be three feet, and also let the depths d and d_1 be equal; then from (108)

$$\frac{\sin \beta}{\tan \alpha} = \left(\frac{2.298}{3.000}\right)^2 = 0.5866.$$

If the approach angle α be taken as 30 degrees, the value of the exit angle β to satisfy this equation is 19° 48′, and from (109) the hydraulic efficiency is 0.899. If, however, α be 24 degrees, the value of β is 15° 08′ and the hydraulic efficiency is 0.941; these values of α and β will hence be selected.

The depth d is to be chosen so that the given quantity of water may pass out of the guide orifices with the proper velocity. This velocity is, from (107),

$$v_0 = 24.06/\cos 24° = 26.34 \text{ feet per second};$$

and hence the area of the guide orifices should be

$$a_0 = 120/26.34 = 4.556 \text{ square feet},$$

from which the depth of the orifices and wheel is

$$d = 4.556/2\pi r \sin 24° = 0.776 \text{ feet}.$$

As a check on the computations the velocities V and V_1, with the corresponding areas a and a_0, may be found, and d be again determined in two ways. Thus,

$$V = v_0 \sin 24° = 10.71, \quad V_1 = u_1 = ur_1/r = 31.42 \text{ ft. per sec.};$$
$$a = 120/10.71 = 11.204, \quad a_1 = 120/31.42 = 3.820 \text{ square ft.};$$
$$d = 11.204/2\pi r = 0.776, \quad d_1 = 3.820/2\pi r_1 \sin \beta = 0.776 \text{ feet};$$

and this completes the preliminary design, which should now be revised so that the several areas may not include the thickness of the guides and vanes (Art. 160).

Although the hydraulic efficiency of this reaction turbine is 94 per cent, the practical efficiency will probably not exceed 80 per cent. About 2 per cent of the total work will be lost in axle friction. The losses due to the friction of the water in passing through the guides and vanes, together with that of the wheel revolving in water, and perhaps also a loss in leakage, will probably amount to more than one-tenth of the total work. All of these losses influence the economic velocity so that a test would be likely to show that the highest efficiency would obtain for a speed less than 100 revolutions per minute.

ARTICLE 160. GUIDES AND VANES.

The discussions in the last two articles have neglected the thickness of the guides and vanes. As these, however, occupy a considerable space a more correct investigation will here be made to take them into account. Let t be the thickness of a guide and n their number, t_1 the thickness of a vane and n_1 their number. Then the areas a_0, a, and a_1 perpendicular to the directions of v_0, V, and V_1 are strictly

$$a_0 = (2\pi r \sin \alpha - nt)d, \qquad a = (2\pi r \sin \phi - n_1 t_1)d,$$
$$a_1 = (2\pi r_1 \sin \beta - n_1 t_1)d_1;$$

and the expressions in (103) are

$$q = a_0 v_0 = aV = a_1 V_1, \quad . \quad . \quad . \quad . \quad (103)'$$

while those in (105) become

$$\frac{u_1}{v_0} = \frac{a_0}{a_1}, \qquad \frac{u}{v_0} = \frac{a_0 r}{a_1 r_1}; \quad . \quad . \quad . \quad . \quad (105)'$$

also, the necessary condition in (108) is

$$\frac{\sin(\phi - \alpha)}{\sin \phi} = \frac{a_0 r}{a_1 r_1}, \quad . \quad . \quad . \quad . \quad . \quad (108)'$$

and the greatest hydraulic efficiency is given by

$$e = 1 - 2\frac{r_1^2}{r^2} \frac{\sin(\phi - \alpha)}{\sin \phi} \frac{\sin^2 \frac{1}{2}\beta}{\cos \alpha}, \quad . \quad . \quad . \quad (109)'$$

in which, of course, $\sin (\phi - \alpha)/ \sin \phi$ may be replaced by its equivalent $a_0 r/a_1 r_1$. The advantageous speed is, as before, given by (107).

To discuss a special case, let the example of the last article be again taken. An outward-flow turbine is to be designed to use 120 cubic feet of water under a head of 18 feet while making 100 revolutions per minute, the gate being fully opened. The preliminary design has furnished the values $r = 2.298$ feet, $r_1 = 3.000$ feet, $d = d_1 = 0.776$ feet, $\phi = 90°$, $\alpha = 24°$, $\beta = 15° 08'$. It is now required to revise these so that 24 guides and 36 vanes may be introduced. Each of these will be made one-half an inch thick, but on the inner circumference of the wheel the vanes will be thinned or rounded so as to prevent shock and foam that might be caused by the entering water striking against their square ends (see Fig. 122). If the radii and angles remain unchanged the effect of the vanes will be to increase the depth of the wheel, which is now 0.702 feet wide and 0.776 feet deep. As these are good proportions, it will perhaps be best to keep the depth and the radii unchanged, and to see how the angles and the efficiency will be affected.

Since the vanes are to be thinned at the inner circumference the area a is unaltered and its value is simply $2\pi r d \sin \phi$. Hence ϕ remains 90 degrees, and V is unchanged. This requires that the area a should remain the same as before. The area a_1 is also the same, as its value is q/u_1. Accordingly

$$4.556 = (2\pi r \sin \alpha - 24t)d, \quad 3.820 = (2\pi r_1 \sin \beta - 36t_1)d_1,$$

in which α and β are alone unknown. Inserting the numerical values and solving, $\alpha = 28° 26'$ and $\beta = 19° 55'$, both being increased by about $4\frac{1}{2}$ degrees. From (109)' the efficiency is now found to be 0.898, a decrease of 0.043, due to the introduction of the guides and vanes.

The efficiency may be slightly raised by making the outer depth d_1 greater than the inner depth d. For instance, let $d_1 = 0.816$, while d remains 0.776; then β is found to be 19° 06′, and $e = 0.906$. But another way is to thin down the vanes at the exit circumference and thus maintain the full area a_1 with a small angle β. If this be done in the present case d_1 may be kept at 0.776 feet, β be reduced to about 16 degrees, and the efficiency will then be about 0.92 or 0.93.

No particular curve for the guides and vanes is required, but it must be such as to be tangent to the circumferences at the designated angles. The area between two vanes on any cross-section normal to the direction of the velocity should also not be greater than the area at entrance; in order to secure this vanes are frequently made much thicker at the middle than at the ends (see Fig. 122).

ARTICLE 161. DOWNWARD-FLOW TURBINES.

Downward- or parallel-flow turbines are those in which the water passes through the wheel without changing its distance

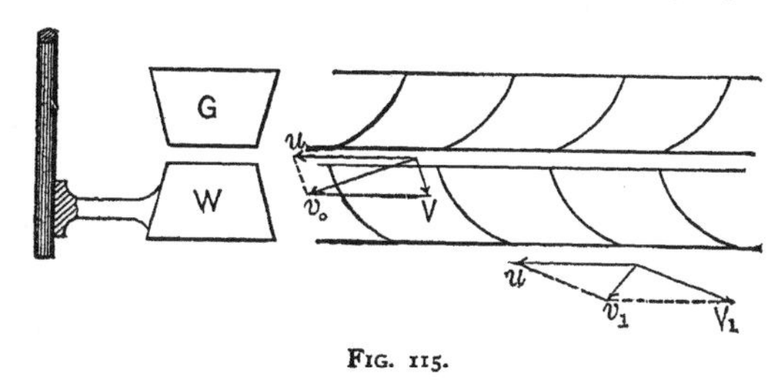

FIG. 115.

from the axis of revolution. In Fig. 115 is a semi-vertical section of the guide and wheel passages, and also a development of a portion of a cylindrical section showing the inner arrangement. The formula for the discharge can be adapted to this by making $u_1 = u$. In this turbine there is no action of centrifugal force, so that the relative exit velocity V_1 is equal to V.

The great advantage of this form of turbine is that it can be set some distance above the tail race and still obtain the power due to the total fall. This distance cannot exceed 34 feet, the height of the water barometer, and usually it does not exceed 25 feet. Fig. 116 shows in a diagramatic way a cross-section of the penstock P, the guide passages G, the wheel W, and the air-tight draught tube T, from which the water escapes by a gate E to the tail race. The pressure-head H_1 on the exit orifices is here negative, so that the air pressure equivalent to this head is added to the water pressure in the penstock, and hence the discharge through the guides occurs as if the wheel were set at the level of the tail race. Strictly speaking a vacuum, more or less complete, is formed just below the wheel into which the water drops with a low absolute velocity, having surrendered to the wheel nearly all its energy. Short draught tubes are also often used with inward-flow turbines.

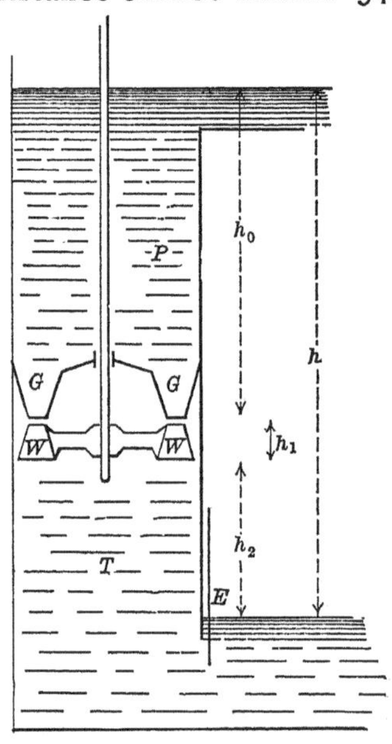

FIG. 116.

Let h be the total head between the water levels in the head and tail races, h_0 the depth of the entrance orifices of the wheel below the upper level, h_1 the vertical height of the wheel, and h_2 the height of the exit orifices above the tail race; so that $h = h_0 + h_1 + h_2$. Let H and H_1 be the heads which measure the absolute pressures at the entrance and exit orifice of the wheel and h_a the height of the water barometer. Let v_0 be the absolute velocity with which the water leaves the guides and enters the vanes, and V and V_1 the relative velocities at entrance and exit. Then from Article 27

$$v_0^2 = 2g(h_a + h_0 - H),$$

$$V_1^2 = V^2 + 2g(h_1 + H - H_1).$$

Adding these two equations there results

$$v_0^2 - V^2 + V_1^2 = 2g(h_0 + h_1 + h_a - H_1).$$

But $h_a - H_1$ is equal to h_2, and hence

$$v_0^2 - V^2 + V_1^2 = 2gh. \quad . \quad . \quad . \quad . \quad . \quad . \quad . \quad . \quad . \quad (101)'$$

This formula is the same as (101) if u be made equal to u_1, and hence all the formulas of the last three articles apply to the downward-flow reaction turbine by placing $u = u_1$, and $r^1 = r_1$.

Let r be the mean radius and u the mean velocity of the entrance and exit orifices of the wheel, let d be the width of the entrance orifices and d_1 that of the exit orifices. Let α be the approach angle which the direction of the entering water makes with that of the velocity u, or the angle which the guides make with the upper plane of the wheel (Fig. 116); let ϕ be the entrance angle which the vanes make with that plane, and β the acute exit angle which they make with the lower plane. Then the values of the advantageous velocity u and the entering velocity v_0 are

$$u = \sqrt{\frac{gh \sin(\phi - \alpha)}{\cos\alpha \sin\phi}}, \qquad v_0 = \sqrt{\frac{gh \sin\phi}{\cos\alpha \sin(\phi - \alpha)}}, \quad (107)'$$

and the necessary relation between the angles and dimensions of the wheel is

$$\frac{\sin(\phi - \alpha)}{\sin \phi} = \frac{d \sin \alpha}{d_1 \sin \beta} = \frac{a_0}{a_1}, \quad . \quad . \quad . \quad . \qquad (108)'$$

while the hydraulic efficiency is

$$e = 1 - 2\frac{a_0}{a_1}\frac{\sin^2 \frac{1}{2}\beta}{\cos \alpha} = 1 - \frac{d}{d_1} \tan \alpha \tan \tfrac{1}{2}\beta. \quad . \qquad (109)'$$

To these equations is to be added the condition that the pressure-head H_1 cannot be less than that of a vacuum, and on account of air leakage it must be practically greater; thus

$$H_1 > 0, \quad h_a - h_2 > 0, \quad h_2 < h_a;$$

that is, the height of the wheel orifices above the tail race must be less than the height of the water barometer.

As an example of design, let $\phi = 90°$ and $\alpha = 30°$. Then $u = \sqrt{gh}$, or the velocity due to one-half the head; and $v_0 = \sqrt{\frac{4}{3}gh}$, or a velocity due to two-thirds of the head. From (108)′ taking $d_1 = \frac{3}{2}d$, the value of β is 22° 38′, and from (109)′ the efficiency is 0.92. This value will be lowered by the introduction of guides and vanes, as well as by friction and the energy carried away by the water as it escapes through the gate into the tail race, so that perhaps not more than 0.80 will be obtained in practice.

ARTICLE 162. IMPULSE TURBINES.

Whenever a turbine is so arranged that the channels between the vanes are not fully filled with water, it ceases to act as a reaction turbine and becomes an impulse turbine.

A turbine set above the level of the tail race becomes an impulse turbine when the gate is partially lowered, unless the gates are arranged over the exit orifices.

The velocity with which the water leaves the guides in an impulse turbine is simply $\sqrt{2gh_0}$ where h_0 is the head on the guide orifices. The rules and formulas in Art. 151 apply in all respects, and for a well-designed wheel the entrance angle ϕ is double the approach angle α, the best speed and corresponding hydraulic efficiency are

$$u = \sqrt{\frac{gh_0}{2\cos^2\alpha}}, \qquad e = 1 - \left(\frac{r_1 \sin\frac{1}{2}\beta}{r\cos\alpha}\right)^2,$$

while the discharge is $q = a_0\sqrt{2gh_0}$ and the work per second is $k = wqh_0e$.

As an example, suppose that the reaction turbine designed in Art. 159 were to act as an impulse turbine, and the angles α and β remaining at 24° and 15° 08′, the radii r and r_1 being 2.298 and 3.000 feet. It would then be necessary that ϕ should be 48° instead of 90° in order to secure the best results. Under a head of 18 feet the velocity of flow from the guides would be 34.02 feet per second instead of 26.34 The velocity of the inner circumference would be 18.63 feet per second instead of 24.06, so that the number of revolutions per minute would be about 77 instead of 100. The efficiency would be 0.96, or almost exactly the same as before. If, however, the angle ϕ were to remain 90° the efficiency would be materially lowered, since then the water could not enter tangentially to the vanes and a loss in impact would necessarily result.

Impulse turbines move slower than reaction turbines under the same head, but the relative entrance velocity V is greater, and hence more energy is liable to be spent in shock and foam. In impulse turbines the entrance angle ϕ should be double the approach angle α, but in reaction turbines it is often greater than 3α, and its value depends upon the exit angle β: hence the vanes in impulse turbines are of sharper curvature for the same values of α and β. In impulse turbines the efficiency is not lowered by a partial closing of the gates, whereas the sudden enlargement of section causes a material loss in reaction turbines. The advantageous speed of an impulse turbine remains the same for all positions of the gate, but with a reaction turbine it is very much slower at part gate than at full gate. For many kinds of machinery it is important to maintain a constant speed for different amounts of power, and with a reaction turbine this can only be done by a great loss in efficiency. When the water supply is low the impulse turbine hence has a marked advantage in efficiency. A further merit of the impulse turbine is that it may be arranged so that water enters only through a part of the guides, while this is impossible in reaction turbines. On the other hand, reaction turbines can be set below the level of the tail race or above it, using a draught tube in the latter case, and still secure the power due to the total fall, whereas an impulse turbine must always be set above the tail-race level and loses all the fall between that level and the guide orifices.

ARTICLE 163. SPECIAL DEVICES.

Many devices to increase the efficiency of reaction turbines, particularly at part gate, have been proposed. In the Fourneyron turbine a common plan is to divide the wheel into three parts by horizontal partitions between the vanes so that these are completely filled with water when the gate is either one-third or two-thirds closed (see Fig. 121). The surface exposed to friction is thus, however, materially increased at full gate.

The Boyden diffuser is another device used with outward-flow reaction turbines. This consists of a fixed wooden

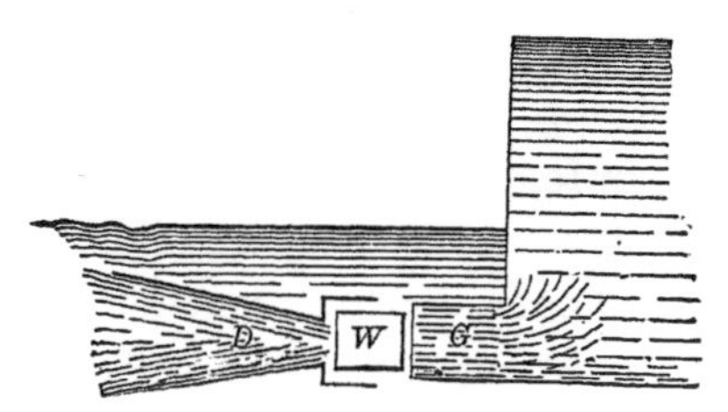

FIG. 117.

annular frame D placed around the wheel W, through which the water must pass after exit from the wheel. Its width is about four or five times that of the wheel, and at the outer end its depth becomes about double that of the wheel. The effect of this is like a draught tube, and although the absolute velocity of the water when issuing from the wheel is greater than before, the absolute velocity of the water coming out of the diffuser is less, and hence a greater amount of energy is imparted to the turbine. It has been shown above that the efficiency of a reaction turbine is increased by making the exit depth d_1 greater than the entrance depth d, and it is seen that the fixed diffuser produces the same result. By the use of this diffuser BOYDEN increased the efficiency of the Fourneyron reaction turbine several per cent.

The pneumatic turbine of GIRARD was devised to overcome the loss in reaction turbines due to a partial closing of the gate. The turbine was enclosed in a kind of bell into which air could be pumped, thus lowering the tail water level around the wheel. At part gate this pump is put into action, and as a consequence the air is admitted into the wheel, and the water flowing through it does not fill the spaces between the vanes. Hence the action becomes like that of an impulse turbine, and the full efficiency is maintained. A wheel thus arranged should properly have the entrance angle ϕ double the approach angle α in order that the advantageous speed may be always the same.

Turbines without guides have been used. Here the approach angle α is probably about 90 degrees, as the water would probably approach the wheel by the shortest path. The entrance angle ϕ would then be made greater than 90 degrees, and the reliance for high efficiency must be upon a small value of the exit angle β. But as this can scarcely be made smaller than 15 degrees the hydraulic efficiency will rarely exceed 80 per cent, which by friction and foam will in practice be reduced to about 65 per cent.

The screw turbine consists of one or two turns of a helicoidal surface around a vertical shaft, the screw being enclosed in a cylindrical case. At the point of entrance the downward pressure of the water can be resolved into two components, a relative velocity V parallel to the surface and a horizontal velocity u which corresponds to the velocity of the wheel. At the point of exit it can be resolved in like manner into V_1 and u_1. But, as in other cases, the condition for high efficiency is $u_1 = V_1$, and since the water moves parallel to the axis, $u_1 = u$. Applying the general formulas (99)–(101), it is seen that this can only occur when the head h is zero or when the velocity u is infinite. The screw turbine is hence like a reaction wheel, and high efficiency can never practically be obtained.

ARTICLE 164. THE NIAGARA TURBINES.

A number of turbines have been installed at Niagara for the utilization of a portion of the power of the great falls. Those to be here briefly described are the three large wheels designed by FAESCH and PICARD, of Geneva, Switzerland, and erected in 1894 and 1895 by the Cataract Construction Company. The entire plant is to include ten twin outward-flow reaction turbines, each of 5000 horse-power.

The power plant is located about 1¼ miles above the village of Niagara Falls, where a canal leads the water from the river to the wheel pit. The water is carried down the pit through steel penstocks to the turbines, which are placed 136 feet below the water level in the canal. After passing through the wheels the waste water is conveyed to the river below the American fall by a tunnel 7000 feet long.

Fig. 118 shows part of a longitudinal section of the wheel pit and a side view of two of the penstocks, with the enclosing cases and shafts of the turbines. Fig. 119 shows a cross-section of the wheel pit with an end view of a penstock, wheel case, and shaft. The width of the wheel pit is 20 feet at the top and 16 feet at the bottom, and the cylindrical penstock is 7½ feet in diameter. The shaft of the turbine is a steel tube 38 inches in diameter, built in three sections, and connected by short solid steel shafts 11 inches in diameter which revolve in bearings. At the top of each shaft is a dynamo for generating the electric power.

In Fig. 120 is shown a vertical section of the lower part of the penstock, shaft, and twin wheels. The water fills the casing around the shaft, passes both upward and downward to the guide passages, marked *G*, through which it enters the two wheels, causes them to revolve, and then drops down to

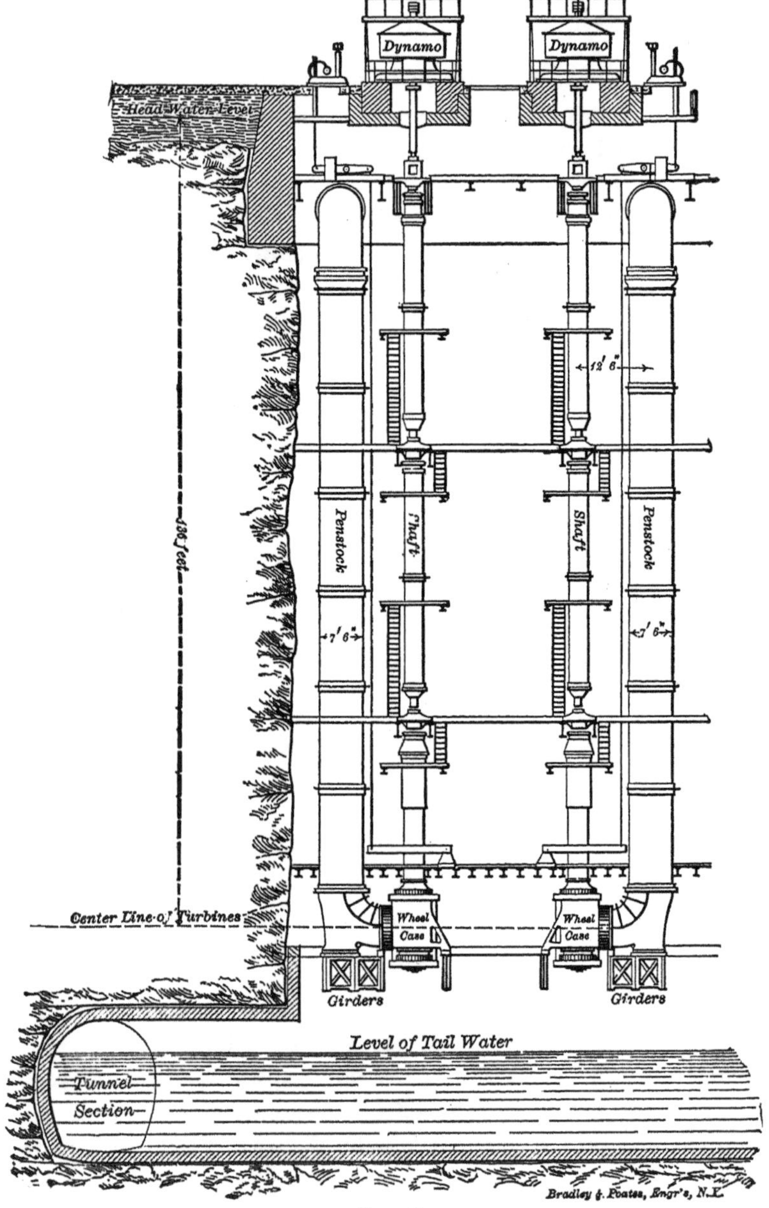
Dynamo
Dynamo
Head Water Level
12' 6"
136 feet
Penstock
Shaft
Shaft
Penstock
7' 6"
7' 6"
Center Line of Turbines
Wheel
Case
Wheel
Case
Girders
Girders
Level of Tail Water
Tunnel
Section
Bradley & Poates, Engr's, N.Y.

FIG. 118.

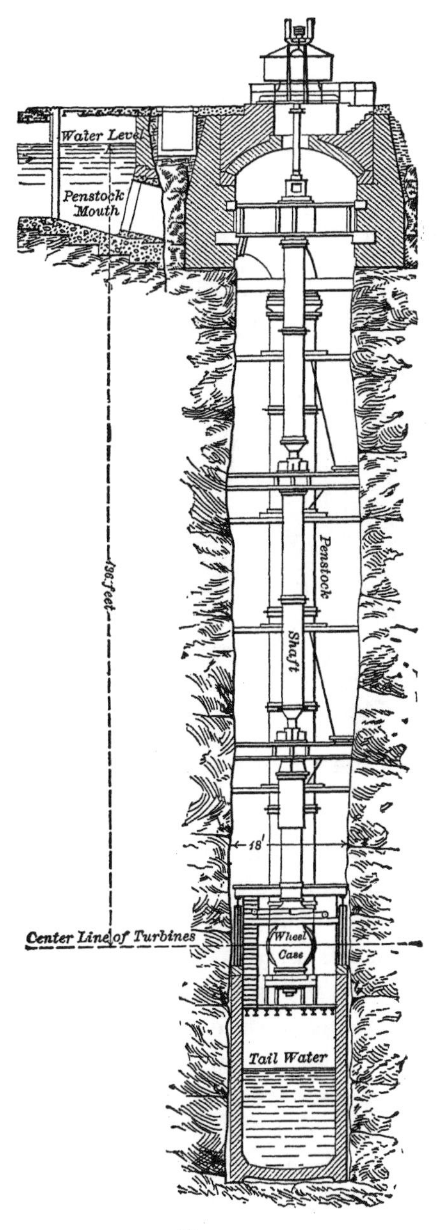
Water Level
Penstock Mouth
136 feet
Penstock
Shaft
18'
Center Line of Turbines
Wheel Case
Tail Water

FIG. 119.

the tail race at the entrance to the tunnel, which carries it away to the river. The gate for regulating the discharge is seen upon the outside of the wheels.

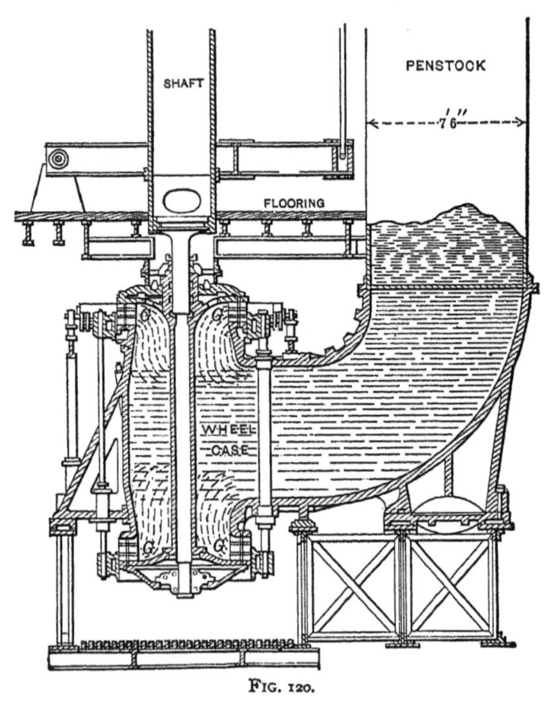

Fig. 120.

Fig. 121 gives a larger vertical section of the lower wheel with the guides, shaft, and connecting members. The guide passages, marked *G*, and the wheel passages, marked *W*, are triple, so that the latter may be filled not only at full gate, but also when it is one-third or two-thirds opened, thus avoiding the loss of energy due to sudden enlargement of the flowing stream. The two horizontal partitions in the wheel are also advantageous in strengthening it. The inner radius of the wheel is 31½ inches and the outer radius is 37½ inches, while the depth is about 12 inches. In this figure the gates are represented as closed.

In Fig. 122 is shown a half-plan of one of the wheels, on a part of which are seen the guides and vanes, there being 36 of the former and 32 of the latter. The value of the approach angle α is 19° 06′, the mean value of the entrance angle ϕ is 110° 40′, and the exit angle β is 13° 17½′. Although the

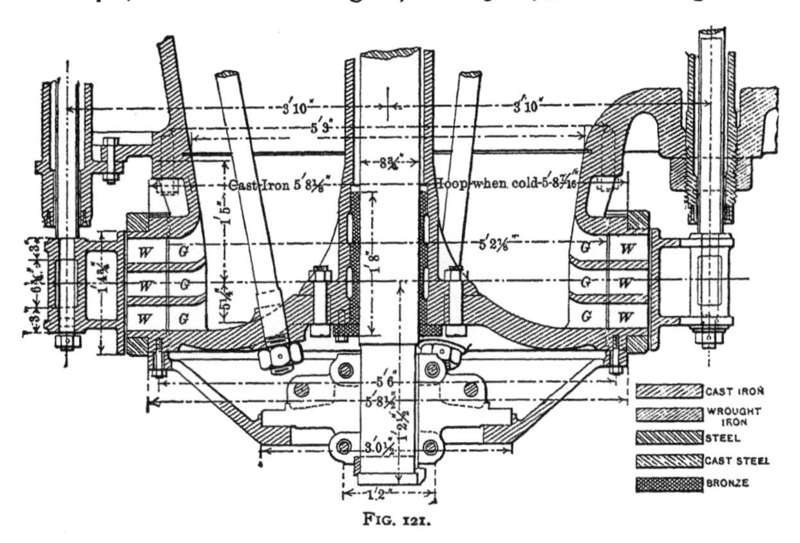

FIG. 121.

water on leaving the wheel is discharged into the air, the very small annular space between the guides and vanes, together with the decreasing area between the vanes from the entrance to the exit orifices, will ensure that the wheels will act like reaction turbines for the three positions of the gates corresponding to the three horizontal stages.

The estimated discharge of one of these twin turbines is about 430 cubic feet per second, and the theoretic power due to this discharge is 6645 horse-powers. Hence if 5000 horse-powers be utilized the efficiency is 75.2 per cent. Under this discharge the mean velocity in the penstock will be nearly 10 feet per second, but the loss of head due to friction in the penstock will be but a small fraction of a foot. The pressure-head in the wheel case will then be practically that due to the actual static head, or closely 141½ feet upon the lower and 130 feet upon the upper wheel. Although the penstock is smaller in section than generally thought necessary for such a large discharge, the loss of head that occurs in it is insignifi-

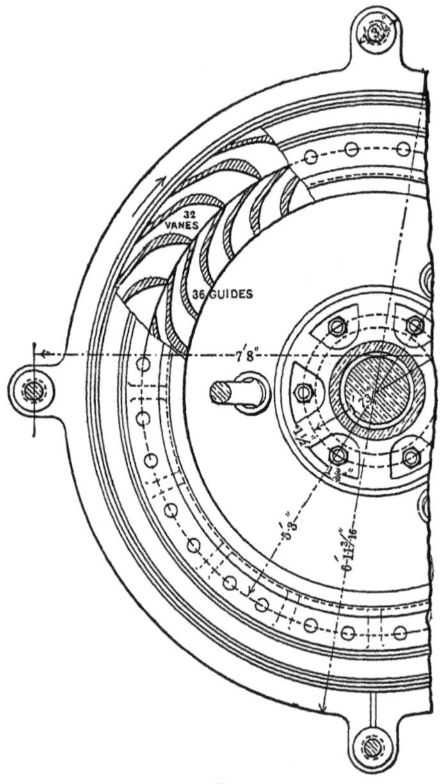

FIG. 122.

cant; and it will be seen in Fig. 118 to be connected with the head canal and with the wheel case by easy curves, and that its section is enlarged in making these approaches.

From formula (107) the advantageous velocity of the inner circumference of the upper wheel, taking $h = 130\frac{1}{2}$ feet, is found to be 64.88 feet per second, and that for the lower wheel, taking $h = 141\frac{1}{2}$ feet, is found to be 71.73 feet per second. Perhaps the mean of these, or 70.31 feet per second, will closely correspond with the advantageous velocity for the two combined. The number of revolutions per minute for the condition of maximum efficiency will then be closely 250. The absolute velocity of the water when entering the wheel will be about 66 feet per second, so that the pressure-head in the guide passages of the upper wheel will be nearly 66 feet. The mean absolute velocity of the water when leaving the wheels is about 19 feet per second, so that the loss due to this is only about 4 per cent of the total head.

The weight of the dynamo, shaft, and turbine is carried, when the wheels are in motion, by the upward pressure of the water in the wheel case on a piston placed above the upper wheel. The upper disk containing the guides is, for this purpose, perforated, so that the water pressure can be transmitted through it. The lower disk, on the other hand, is solid, and the weight of the water upon it is carried by inclined rods upward to the wheel case, which together with the penstock is supported upon several girders. At the upper end of the shaft is a thrust bearing to receive the excess of vertical pressure, which may be either upward or downward under different conditions of power and speed.

A governor is provided for the regulation of the speed, and this is located on the surface near the dynamo. It is of the centrifugal-ball type, and so connected with the main shaft and the turbine gates that the latter are partially closed whenever from any cause the speed increases. These gates are so set that the orifices of the upper and lower wheels are not simultaneously closed, one gate being in advance of the other by about the width of one division stage. The revolving field magnets of the dynamo also serve as a fly-wheel for equalizing the speed. With this method of regulation it is expected that the speed cannot increase more than three or four per cent when 25 per cent of the work is suddenly removed.

These turbines were designed by the Swiss engineers above named, after an international competition in which three Swiss, one Austrian, four French, three English, and two American firms participated. Three of the turbines were installed in 1895, and the erection of six others was completed in 1898.*

---

* See Engineering News, Jan. 23, 1892, and March 30, 1893; also an article by HERSCHEL in Cassiers' Magazine for March, 1893. For many of the above facts the author is indebted to the kindness of the officers of the Cataract Construction Company, through Dr. COLEMAN SELLERS, President and Chief Engineer of the Niagara Falls Power Company.